D1291610

THE MAKING OF A SCIENTIST

By RAYMOND L. DITMARS

CONFESSIONS OF A SCIENTIST
THE FOREST OF ADVENTURE
REPTILES OF THE WORLD
SNAKES OF THE WORLD
THRILLS OF A NATURALIST'S QUEST
THE WHYS ON EARTH
THE MAKING OF A SCIENTIST

A tiny pond—and the only pond—on the island of Trinidad where one of the world's strangest frogs completes its life cycle.

THE MAKING OF A SCIENTIST

BY

RAYMOND L. DITMARS

NEW YORK

THE MACMILLAN COMPANY

1937

Set up and electrotyped. Published September, 1937.

FIRST PRINTING

PRINTED IN THE UNITED STATES OF AMERICA
BY THE STRATFORD PRESS, INC., NEW YORK

To

JOHN B. STANCHFIELD

FELLOW ADVENTURER ON MANY SAILING TRIPS
AND A RECONNOITER TO TRINIDAD

INTRODUCTION

THIS is a book about a scientist's good times, and some of his disappointments. There has been no intention of guiding the writing to point a moral from the theme, although the reader may sense that there is one. The theme is based upon an early discussion with my father who took strong exception to what he considered the vacillating interests of his young son, partly because he feared that they might continue into manhood. As time went on our intimate contact brought about a sympathetic understanding, but others, without his knowledge of me, had much to advise about concentration along a one-track line. If I had followed all the advice I have received I am convinced that the world would have seemed a smaller place than I have found it.

R. L. D.

ACKNOWLEDGMENTS

THE author and the publishers wish to extend credit and thankful acknowledgment for photographs received from the extensive files of the New York Zoölogical Society, through the courtesy of William Bridges, Editor and Curator of Publications. The close-up of the rare pygmy marmoset was provided by Dr. Wolfgang von Hagen, who brought this animal from Ecuador. The scenes of clouds were sent to the author by the late William A. Bentley.

CONTENTS

ILLUSTRATIONS

ILLUSTRATIONS

THE MAKING OF A SCIENTIST

Chapter I

EPISODE OF THE THOUSAND FLIES

It was the day of New York's biggest parade—the Columbian Celebration. Militia converged on the city from various states. The corps of Barnard School, which I attended, was marching into a side street, from Fifth Avenue, to fall into a part of the military school division that would be fed into the parade. The order came for short step.

Shove—shove—shove—shove went the feet.

The file ahead looked like a gray wall on white posts which bent and swung as if moved by the rhythm of machinery. Ahead of us was one of New York's crack drum corps, forty pieces, spaced from curb to curb. In our uniforms we felt important and impressive, and as if we were stepping on air.

As the column slowed down, I spoke to Ben Cullen:

"I've saved enough lunch money to buy that water snake at Eggeling's bird store."

"The one in the window?"

"Yes, he's had it a month."

On our right stretched a motionless wall of gray,

gray from head to foot. It was West Point at rest. Each cadet seemed a head taller than we. The line bulged from the curb, but our guide sergeants relentlessly moved straight ahead, squeezing it back.

"Nice boys," came the patronizing voice of a West Pointer.

"No talking in the ranks," said another, whose ornate stripes stretched from elbow to shoulder. He directed a stern glance at Cullen and me.

"Shut up, you big stiff, you're talking yourself," came from our ranks.

The column marched on.

That was a great day for all of us boys. Finally we swung into Fifth Avenue, through miles of color, to music that thrilled the youthful heart. We came out of it, with its crowds and grandstands, rather breathless. But there was still a high spot of the day: I was going to buy that water snake.

Getting rid of my rifle, shedding white trousers for gray, coming home and reporting to my parents brought the time nearly to the evening meal before I could go to Eggeling's bird store. My family were going over to the Hudson to see the illumination of battleships from all nations, a spectacle they said I might never have another chance to see. I insisted that I must go to Eggeling's or somebody might buy the snake. My collection of serpents up to that moment consisted of only two little garter snakes, admitted to the household after prolonged discussion as to the innocence of all members of the garter snake group. Possibly I had been naïve in swinging my arguments by mentioning a "group." I had thoughts of gradually introducing relatives of the garter snakes. At any rate that was how permission had been reluctantly granted to add the water snake to the collection. I showed my father a scientific list in which the genus *Thamnophis* (garter snakes) and *Tropidonotus* (water snakes) brushed shoulders in relationship. He examined the list very critically, then asked where the rattlesnakes and copperheads came in. I turned many pages before arriving at their genera, and he grudgingly admitted that they seemed to be separated by quite a procession of names, though some of these looked alarming enough.

One other reason for desiring the family to go to the Hudson while I bought the water snake was my doubt about their accepting it as a member in good standing of the "garter snake group." That snake at Eggeling's was close to four feet long and two inches thick. The garter snakes were no thicker than my little finger. Moreover, they were gentle and my family was resigned to see me handle them. The prospective purchase was quick and ugly, and had struck at me the last time I had been to see it. I figured I would have a tussle with the snake, when I got it home, to get it into a cage already built, and I didn't want that tussle to be witnessed by my family.

At Eggeling's bird store I paid three dollars for the

water snake, in quarters and dimes saved from my daily lunch allowance of thirty-five cents. Saving up for the purchase of the snake, I had eaten luncheons consisting of a coffee ring and a glass of milk. On a few occasions, when my appetite was overpowering, there had been two coffee rings.

Mr. Otto Eggeling, a rotund and affable German, debated on the best method of transferring the water snake. He hit upon the plan of tying a burlap bag to the top of the terrarium, inverting the container and dropping moss, pebbles and serpent into the bag. In this way I obtained background accessories along with my purchase. I hurried through the side streets of Harlem with the bag, and reached our apartment without attracting attention. The maid had slipped out and the coast was clear. I had not worried particularly about her being there, for she almost always went out as soon as the family did.

With my pulse beating fast, I brought the water snake's cage into the kitchen. Then I laid the bag on the floor and slid back the glass front of the cage. Cautiously untying Mr. Eggeling's firm knot, I upended the bag, expecting that the snake would emerge quietly, while I manipulated a broom handle to guide it to its quarters. The emergence was precipitate, and the water snake lay coiled on the oilcloth.

I was shocked at its formidable size as compared with its dimensions in the show window. It was quite out of proportion to what I had described to my father as a member of the garter snake group. True enough, according to Professor Cope's list, this was an "innocuous natracine snake," but it flattened out as broad as my hand and made a vicious swipe at my foot. Then it started across the oilcloth with a swishing sound as it tried to gain purchase on the smooth surface.

In those days the vertical pipes leading to kitchen boilers had generous floor openings. With a gasp of apprehension I headed the reptile off with the broom. I managed to sweep the snake toward its cage and it thrashed in. Carrying the cage to the little room allotted to my specimens, I turned its face toward the wall and went to bed. Delay in introducing the reptile to the family seemed advisable. I was thrilled at having it, but I realized that instead of advancing one step at a time as a collector, I had jumped about six—probably more than the family would tolerate. That schoolboy episode with a harmless snake was more thrilling than later experiences with mambas and cobras.

When my father asked to see the new specimen, I said that it was nervous and should rest for a while undisturbed. The face of its cage remained against the wall. When nobody was around I had long and satisfactory looks at it. Going down to the north lake at Central Park, I skirted the marginal grass (watching for a prowling policeman), plucked up a big green-headed frog and took it home to the water snake. The way the snake gobbled up that frog and darted its head from side to side for additional morsels made me apprehensive as to my further dodging of policemen. At any rate, the turning of the cage front to the wall was becoming mysterious. Something had to be done.

Outside of my room was a fire escape. I decided to make a sort of sun porch as an extension of the water snake's cage and to place the outfit at the end of the fire escape. It was my idea that if the snake were first seen from the end of the fire escape it wouldn't look so big. The outfit was constructed during a feverishly active afternoon, while my mother was out shopping and the maid, as usual, had slipped out. By this time, I think, my father had decided that the water snake was an innocuous specimen, not worthy to be called to the family's attention.

While he may have considered at first that the fire escape or sun-bathing arrangement housed a harmless and languishing thing, he quickly received a shock that made him think differently, and which bounded back on me.

A policeman appeared at our door with a long envelope containing a combination complaint from the police and health departments. When the formal-looking letter was read everyone talked at once.

It appeared that neighbors had peeked from back windows and seen the big snake spread out, enjoying the sun. The sun porch, extending from its cage, was of light framework and covered with fly-screen. The police complaint was to the effect that we were harboring a highly dangerous creature under conditions from which it might escape. The health board protested that the spectacle of a big snake had so shocked several of the neighbors that they were ill and had refused to recover until the nuisance was removed.

Sternly my father told me to bring my contrivance in from the fire escape and when, for the first time, he saw that water snake, he hit the ceiling. His orders were to lock the serpent in the room where the two little garter snakes reposed, and in the morning to take the entire snake contingent back to Eggeling's.

My battle had been lost, and I retreated to my room that night and cried. My only consolation was in hearing the caustic remarks my mother made about the neighbors.

Not seeing the necessity of taking my father's whole command literally, I carried the garter snakes to the then wild northwestern portion of Central Park and watched them glide into the cleft of a ledge—and I didn't leave until their tails had disappeared. Then I returned to the house, battled the water snake into a pillow case, put this in a satchel, and sadly wended my way to Eggeling's. There I told my story.

The German was a kindly old man. We had become acquainted through my hanging around his shop and looking in his windows. He suggested that I start a collection of frogs; there could be no objection to such specimens. The idea seemed rather flat, but he took me along a line of terraria, showed me some big bull frogs,

European pond frogs, pickerel frogs, leopard frogs and the like, and I half-heartedly helped him to pack some of them into containers with moss and started home. The family received the news of my exchange without comment. Frogs were frogs and would not be likely to rouse the ire of the police and health departments.

In an effort to rouse some enthusiasm for the frogs, or at least to make them comfortable, I built an elaborate apartment for them. It was four feet long and had screen windows. The partitions didn't extend quite to the top, the idea being to allow an overhead runway for flies, which I planned to feed to the frogs. Little did I realize that, in spite of the family's passive acceptance of this indisputably innocent, goggle-eyed collection, the frogs were to usher in a tragedy more appalling than the incident of the water snake.

My plan for feeding the frogs was to make a master fly trap, catch a goodly batch of the insects, introduce the top of the trap at a circular door at the end of the elongated frog enclosure, and knock off the cover. The flies would then circulate from one apartment to the other, past the tops of the partitions—which, as I have said, did not quite reach the ceiling of the cage. For a quarter I bought a fly trap at the hardware store, a cylindrical affair, tapering toward the top. This was a miniature model for what I planned to build, with wooden base and window-screen top. The miniature was duplicated, in relative outline, by a contrivance two feet high. With it, I set forth to what I considered the best place for flies, Quinn's Livery Stable on 124th Street, where I had gone many times to look at the horses. As bait for the trap, I had extracted a slab of steak from the refrigerator.

While the stableman was surprised at my contrivance and explanation, he was friendly and interested, and the trap was placed on a window near the stalls.

Stopping at the stable the next day on my way from school, I was delighted. The trap looked like a beehive. There were ordinary flies, medium-sized and blue-bottles. As I picked it up, it roared. The stableman told me to come back at any time—there were plenty more. Thinking that such a collection might be of undue interest to pedestrians, I asked for a page of newspaper and the trap was thus covered.

When I got home I thought it best to change the water in the frog basins first, then make each apartment spick and span before turning in the flies, so that the frogs might have uninterrupted enjoyment for a day or so. This servicing took time, and the dinner hour was close at hand, but I was determined to see the frogs fed before I was called to such ordinary business as the evening meal.

Going to my room where the paper-encased trap had been left, I started to remove the covering. In pulling off the paper, my finger caught on the door of the contrivance and pulled it open.

I shall never forget the ascending swarm of insects that roared past my face. After the first moment of realizing the catastrophe, I dashed to close the door, but my room was rather dark and the legions had streamed into the lighted hallway, and had distributed themselves throughout the house. Each room seemed more populous than the stalls of Quinn's Livery Stable. The murmuring hum was incessant, punctuated by the higher tone and bumping-against-the-ceilings of the blue-bottle flies, delectable to frogs, but agonizing in an apartment. This was the situation my father encountered when he arrived home from business, and his introduction to the servicing of a collection of frogs.

As we attempted to get through the evening meal, with flies over everything, the atmosphere grew tragic. An examination of the bed rooms, with their fly-covered ceilings and spreads, broke down the last vestige of family toleration. I was sent scudding for boxes of fly paper. Soon the rooms looked as if soiled wash had been suspended, while bureaus and tables were carpeted with entangling sheets. A few flies were caught that way. With a sense about the ways of insects that was later to be developed in a legitimate entomological department, I observed that the invaders preferred to fly high. That was not the case, however, when the family retired. The flies crawled over faces and buzzed around ears. I pulled the sheet over my head and slept the sleep of youth, with occasional awaking, akin to nightmare, marred by thoughts of what would happen the next day.

Breakfast was a solemn affair, well attended by flies.

Many decorated the ceiling, resting after the buzzing orgy of the night. Parental action came swift and relentless. The frogs must go. And that was the end of my collection.

There was a lapse of many months before I could bring anything alive back into that little room. Finally I got some small lizards from Eggeling's which were demonstrated to eat mealworms, kept in a can. A land crab was later scrutinized and admitted, as being a vegetarian. No snakes came into the household again until several years after I had started as apprentice at the American Museum of Natural History, and had written a scientific paper which proved that what I was trying to do was accepted as legitimate by the scientific world.

The job with the Museum, which completely changed my life, almost dropped out of the sky. It came about chiefly through a tendency for which my father criticized me, as did friends in later life—to follow a variety of enthusiasms. Among boyhood interests, some of which I admit detracted from my work at school, was the subject of entomology. I was especially interested in beetles and moths. My moth collection occupied several picture frames which I had deepened by a rear extension to make room for pinned specimens. I had been to the Museum several times to visit Curator Beutenmüller, in the Department of Entomology, to have a puzzling specimen identified. I realized that the curator endured, rather than enjoyed, this invasion of youth, and so I never stayed more than five minutes.

One afternoon I went to the Museum with several specimens of a small moth which intrigued me. I knew its scientific name, which was *Utetheisa bella*. It was a beautiful thing, with a wing-span of not much over an inch. The upper wings were snow white, with black dots, as if stippled with a pen. The lower wings were pink. What puzzled me was a variation of hue in the lower wings, which ranged from pale pink almost to red. I could find but one species of *Utetheisa* listed for the Northeastern States. My question was about the reddish ones. I had noticed that some varieties of insects had distinct scientific names, but nothing of the kind occurred with *Utetheisa*.

The curator plucked one of my pinned insects from the little box, held the pin between his fingers and turned his head to one side.

"It's a bit dark," he said, "but some variation is natural. I haven't seen many. It's not a common thing around here."

"But I have about twenty," I insisted. "I got them on the Palisades."

"Twenty specimens of *Utetheisa?*" He leaned back in his chair.

"Yes, sir. I've pinned them to show the variation from pink to red."

The chief swung forward and picked up a pen.

"Bring them in some day," he said, dismissing me.

I felt that my statement had been received with doubt.

I brought them in on the following day. There was no doubt about the scientist's interest. He spent fully ten minutes looking over the specimens.

"Who mounted these specimens?"

"I did, sir. I used fine needles to keep from making holes in the wings."

He picked up a small magnifying glass and bent close to the specimens.

"I see you kept close to the fork of venation in pulling up the wing."

"Yes, sir. I've found that if you keep the pin close to the fork it won't slip and tear the wing."

"I'm looking for a young man to mount a large series of moths and butterflies in this department," said the chief. "There will be a chance of working up in the Museum."

His remarks swept me off my feet. I could do little more than stammer that I would like to do it, that I would consult my parents and come back to see him.

You can imagine how I felt. Though I had the carfare to ride back to Harlem, I kept on walking northward along the west wall of Central Park. I intended to get on the street car when the excitement wore away, but trudging along and thinking, I saw the arc lights flash on at 110th Street and realized I was nearly home.

During a dinner when I was too excited to eat, I broke the news to the family. To my surprise, it was received with calm, but I didn't like that calm. However, I was not then in their bad graces; there had been no police complaint, no repetition of the episode of the thousand flies. I tried to sell the idea of going to the Museum by saying that the school term was nearly over, that while the plan was to prepare me for West Point, there would be a long period of studying ahead and expense for my father. Moreover, an army life would take me away from home and I wouldn't be able to see the family for long stretches of time. What I said was really directed to my mother but neither of them made much comment.

I am convinced that it was my mother who decided the issue and for a reason which I didn't use in my own argument. She came into my room one night while I was studying, pulled down the spread of the bed and patted the pillow. It was a restful gesture and her regular custom. She turned to say good night, then was stopped by seeing my position at the study table.

"Why are you writing with your left hand?"

I was proud of my explanation: I told her that there was a drillmaster and gymnasium instructor at the school, a German, who was very severe in disciplinary measures. Some of the boys didn't like him, but I thought he was great and we were pals. One day in the gym, he had noticed that, as the boys approached overhead apparatus, there was a tendency to advance the right hand. He said this was wrong—that cadets should not be right-handed; that the left hand should be able to do all the things performed by the right. If one was a soldier and lost his right hand in combat, then he had his left hand to work with.

My mother took this explanation somberly, and gave me a good-night kiss on the back of my head.

The school term ended. I received a gold medal for composition, but my marks in languages, English history and mathematics gave me grave concern as to approaching the studies for West Point. Mathematical problems seemed insurmountable to me. To borrow a line from the English magazine, *Punch*, it seemed that something was wrong if it turned out to be right. In this state of mind, I played hard for the Museum job.

Again my mother came into the room to say good night. I was drawing some outlines of moths. My right hand was in my pocket and the pencil was in my left hand, a position I still take. She stiffened as she noticed it, recalling my story of the drillmaster and his advice to the prospective soldier to render both hands of equal use. Long afterward I realized that she pictured distant battles from which a one-handed son might return.

"Mom, don't you think I should take that position at the Museum?"

She said that she and my father were thinking it over.

The next morning at breakfast my mother said: "We have decided that you may take the position at the Museum."

Chapter II

THE PRIVATE LIFE OF ATTACUS YAMA-MAIA

That job at the Museum trained me in responsibility and system. I always arrived a few minutes before nine—the hour for the general employees. The curators came to their offices at ten. Shy and a little nervous on the first day, I listened to instructions about mounting moths and butterflies. The procedure was different from mine at home—when fresh-caught specimens, soft of body, were flattened upon a grooved board, their wings pinned, pressed beneath cardboard strips and left to dry. I was shown boxes of specimens, each in a paper container, which were to be placed in a softening box with pads of wet cloth. They had been dead for some time. By the next day they would be soft, relaxed and ready for mounting. There was little to do on that first day, beyond placing specimens in the softening box. The curator was busy examining series of small insects, and making voluminous notes. With a magnifying glass he gazed at moths pinned on a cork-covered table, and from his muttered remarks I could see that he was closely engrossed. The room was large, with a steel balcony surmounted by innumerable glass-topped drawers. There was an arched doorway leading into an equally large room. Not knowing what else to do, I took a cloth and, sliding out one tray after another, wiped off the glass tops. The trays didn't need cleaning; nevertheless I spent the morning on them. The day seemed interminable, for after lunch the chief told me not to bother dusting cases. I wandered about straightening books on the shelves, piling pamphlets more neatly, with the guilty feeling that I was not earning my salt as an employee of the Museum. This sense of idleness upon the close of the first day of having a job was depressing. I walked all the way home along the west wall of Central Park. The next morning, however, loomed brighter. The specimens in the softening box would provide work throughout the day and I would start moistening a new batch for the day following.

Working in the room adjoining the office, I mounted rows of specimens on the drying boards. Taking off the paper strips, I pinned the moths in cork-bottom trays. A dozen trays were filled, the specimens pinned equidistant in precise rows. Two softening boxes were in use. I would hear the curator stamp in at ten o'clock and his muttered comments over the specimens on his table. Also, from the scratching of his pen I knew that he was doing a great deal of writing. Occasionally, he made audible comments indicating difference of opinion with people whom I took to be scientists in his line.

It was after one of these dissertations that I heard a

bang from the office and realized that the chief had pounded the table. He appeared at the door of my room.

"For two weeks," he declared, "I've been straightening out this group of the *Noctuidae*. Of all the ridiculous, asinine——"

He strode back to his office. "Come in here," he called.

I hastened to his table.

"Do you see the relative lengths of those tibial joints, how the longer ones are haired the entire length, the short ones at the basal portion, the medium ones at both segments? Look how they shape into a key."

His pinning forceps flashed among delicate specimens, shooting them into blocks over the cork surface. The dexterity of his fingers was bewildering. I stood back until the hurdling of insects was over. He shoved a magnifying glass into my hand.

"Look at that!"

I cautiously bent over the little moths. There was a similarity among them, although slight differences of wing patterns showed here and there. Looking at the legs, however, I could see that his quick stabbing into groups had unerringly brought out the points he explained.

He had solved a scientific problem in the analysis and separation of a large group of moths, some of them of high importance because of the damage done by their larvae to the products of mankind.

The chief looked up at me with the light of victory in his eyes.

"I'm going to the printer's," he snapped. "Take care of the office." The door slammed a moment later.

The chief was a hard worker and when he was engaged in a problem, he plunged through obstacles like a torpedo boat cutting the waves. He went full speed ahead until he had mastered it. Then, I discovered, he made a dash for "the printer's." There were, of course, conferences with the contracting printing concern about setting up scientific articles, but I came to sense that certain of these dashes were equivalent to funerals of uncles, aunts and grandparents as get-a-ways for ball games. I sympathized with his diversions and had high respect for his accomplishments.

His trips to the printer's meant a chance for me to prowl among glass-topped trays. What gorgeous things there were in that collection! There were the great bird-winged butterflies of New Guinea, some with green markings like parrot feathers and contrasting bodies like red velvet. Then there were the flashing morphos of tropical America, with scintillating blue wings of dazzling hues. Among them were specimens of *Morpho sulkowski*, looking like the surface of an opal, but, when the case was turned to the light, literally taking fire in their brilliance.

Pulling out tray after tray I came to great moths of Malaysia, with bodies as big as a half-grown rat. What treasure hunts those were, always terminated by my frenzied return to the softening boxes and nimble fingers to make up for lost time.

Sent on various errands about the Museum, I came to meet members of the staff who have risen high in the scientific world. There were Dr. Joel A. Allen, the Curator of Mammalogy, and the rapidly ascending Frank M. Chapman, Curator of Birds. My contacts with the curators of ethnology, archaeology, mineralogy and the like were delayed, since their work was not associated with zoölogical problems. Later, I met Dr. Edmund Otis Hovey, the geologist and mineralogist, through some inquiries I made about weather studies. The eminent doctor, vitally interested in the weather, was surprised to see a youth who took the subject seriously. Quite by accident one morning, I met Professor Henry Fairfield Osborn in one of the long halls. What on earth impelled me to talk about snakes, I don't know, but a friendship was established which was to endure and become a strong, guiding influence. That five minutes' talk was one of the foundation stones of my career, because of his encouragement and the kindly interest he took.

Another member of the staff to whom I look back with admiration and appreciation was Dr. Louis K. Gratacap, Curator of Mineralogy. He had seen me fussing among dusty jars of pickled snakes when my job, as he well knew, was mounting butterflies. A man of Gratacap's lovable vivacity and bubbling good humor had no difficulty in gaining the confidence of a boy. He was fond of my chief and often dropped into our office. He was there one morning when the chief received a detailed order from administration headquarters that sent him striding about the office, with hands under his coat-tails, declaiming to the high heavens against the injustice heaped upon a scientist.

The order read that several curators, of whom he was one, were to present a lecture each week to school teachers, and others who might be interested, on subjects relating to their departments. The lectures were to consume an hour and a quarter, and to be of a popular nature and illustrated with lantern slides.

"With me working on this revision of the *Noctuidae,*" shouted the chief. And he slammed the flat of his hand on the table, which had endured many blows.

"But you can't get away from it," said Gratacap, in a pacifying spirit. "President Jesup has been thinking about a popularized lecture course for some time. I'm to talk about gems."

By next morning the office was in a turmoil. The chief decided to write a script for all his lectures and read every word of it. The first lecture was not so difficult, since it related to methods of studying entomology, collecting, and the like. I dug through an extensive series of lantern slides in Professor Bickmore's department of illustrative records and came back with the glass plates. While a number were nothing more than scenics, the chief was able to use them in discussing similar spots where he had done collecting. He made a fine job of it and gave an interesting lecture, but landed on me hard for inserting scenes of the Palisades, the Berkshires and Catskills when his script didn't fit in with the colorful projections on the screen.

The late afternoon succeeding the lecture was depressing. The chief declared that when he finished this one, he had to write another; and, when that was given, start on a third. The revision of the *Noctuidae* was going to the dogs.

The next lecture, on butterflies and moths, sounded promising for illustrations, but when I had gone through enough lantern slides in Professor Bickmore's department to shingle a house, the collection I brought back was not all that could have been hoped for.

"Junk," said the chief.

"But a lot of them are pretty—and there are some interesting species."

"I want life histories," declared the chief.

"The only thing I found was this series of the cecropia moth."

There was more pacing the office with hands under coat-tails.

"May I suggest, sir," I ventured, "that you explain a number of life histories before the slides come on, then show the slides in sort of a running fire of description. I'll make a list of them to show what is coming. You won't have to write anything—just explain what they are."

The suggestion made a hit because it promised synchronizing the talk with the slides. In the first lecture there had been an embarrassing moment during a discussion of how to collect water beetles when the buzz of the signal for another slide brought on a scene of the Catskills blazing in autumn foliage.

These lectures were bringing the chief and me more closely together. We went into a huddle about the idea of an introduction before the slides. I suggested that he tell about the cocoon construction of a big bombycine moth of southern Japan. *Yama-Maia* was its name, an insect of the mountains where there are high winds or the lash of typhoons. The caterpillar of this species starts its cocoon by selecting a big leaf, then covers the stem with a strong network of silk and extends the network over the bough. This part of the job is to eliminate a chance of the leaf being dislodged by gales. The next operation is to curl the leaf around by sideswung movements and pulling of the head, beneath which is the gland that emits a jet of viscid fluid which instantly becomes silk in contact with the air. With the outline of the bag established, the caterpillar goes over it and smears on a heavy silken veneer. Through this the venation of the leaf stands out, and from the spinning gland the viscid fluid issues in leaf-green color, matching the surface over which it is smeared. This serves as a protection against birds and other enemies because of its resemblance to a leaf.

The leaf has been bent around to form an ovoid chamber. Within it is woven a silken coating as smooth and polished as rubbed bronze; but there are important finishing touches. The top is woven in the form of an elastic escapement, two-sided, to be pushed open with a heave of thorax and shoulders; that flap is a hazard owing to wasp-like parasites who might enter and lay their eggs and whose larvae would consume the helpless mummy-like object. The protection against such invaders is the spinning of a thick fluff of entangling silk within the escapement valve. No wasp or member of the *Ichneumonidae* could get past it.

One more thing needs be done. This is to design a water outlet on the bottom. The valve might admit drops of rain during torrential storms, so a small, circular outlet is left open at the bottom, again protected by silk entanglement against parasites.

The job done, the caterpillar skin is shed and a mummy-like pupa within the cocoon sleeps on to its hour of emergence, when a distended and splitting skin awakens it and it blindly squeezes its way through the escapement valve. Gorgeous wings are unfurled within a few hours and it flies off, with no mouth parts, but big, compound eyes, and highly sensitive antennae like feathers, to seek a mate, to breed and die with battered wings, after the eggs are laid, less than a month from its emergence. Its life as a hungry leaf-eating caterpillar has lasted only a few months of summer, then came the task of spinning the cocoon and a period of insensate encasement. The sun and air again for a few weeks, and life is over—all within a year, from youth to death—a normal continuity.

I suggested this story to the chief as part of his introduction.

"Very good," he assented. "You write that part of it. But don't get sad about the last part. I'm not delivering a sermon. This popular stuff gets my goat."

The reading of the lecture went off very well. Toward the last I slipped up to the rostrum and whispered that there were some fine slides of *Parnassius* at the end—butterflies with wings like glass smoked with frost.

"We forgot to put in the notes about their flying over banks of perpetual snow," I whispered, "the highest flying of all the *Lepidoptera*."

The chief glanced at his watch, which lay in front of him on the illuminated reading table. It read ten minutes past the supposed end of the lecture period.

"The species of *Parnassius* are alpine types, living at high altitudes," he concluded, and I heard the buzzer go z-r-r-r-r-r as the alpine butterflies hit the screen and flashed off again.

The lecture was such a success that a group of school teachers accompanied the chief to the department to see some of the specimens in the trays. He cast a weary look at me and replaced a cigar in his waistcoat pocket.

"That idea of an introduction before the lantern slides works out all right," declared the curator, coming into the mounting room.

"Write out a few more of those things, like *Attacus Yama-Maia*. The next lecture is on odd orders. I'm going to concentrate on the *Hymenoptera* and *Neuroptera*. I've written up the *Hymenoptera* and I'm damned if I'll write any more. I haven't touched those trays of *Noctuidae* in two weeks. Write something about the *Neuroptera*, but cut out the sob stuff. Don't say anything about May flies that live years in the water and only flit around a few hours in the air. I felt like an ass when I read that youth to death stuff in a year about *Attacus*. Write something sensible."

He spoke emphatically but I was glad of a change from the interminable mounting of small specimens. Moreover, it was gratifying to be able to help the chief.

True enough, the history of *Attacus* had been sad. Now, I decided, I must think of some cruel type of insect—and which of these should I take among the *Neuroptera?*

I considered the dragon fly, dashing like a hawk for unfortunate insects of the air; how it began life as an aquatic form, with a mask-like covering of the face, which could be shot forward, to grasp and encase an infant tadpole or water beetle. I described that aquatic, larval form of the dragon fly, but it was not enough—a few paragraphs covered it. Delving through the lists, I stubbed my toe on the very thing: the ant lion.

Here was the cousin of the dragon fly, but instead of starting life in water, the eggs were laid in dusty sand. From its very beginning the creature constructed ensnaring pits, first for minute forms, then for ants and small beetles. The full-grown larva of the common southern species was half an inch long, with globular body, strong legs, flattened head and powerful jaws. The flat head was an important part of its equipment, since it was capable of jerking this head sharply upward.

These larvae lived only in the driest sand. Their pits or snares were under thick-spreading branches of pine trees, beneath shelving banks and the like. This was necessary for their mode of life. In such places could be seen many craters, shaped like the mouth of a funnel and two to three inches in diameter. It was through manipulation of the head that the funnel was constructed, the creature burrowing in a suitable spot then jerking the head upward in throwing out the sand. A pit could be constructed in a few moments' time. If the location of the trap was unfavorable, the ant lion, waiting like a fisherman with a passive line, changed its position—except that a couple of hours to the fisherman would be equal to several days to the ant lion.

The treacherous crater, with its sharply outlined rim brought about the fate of wandering insects. A step near the edge, and it gave way. In vain the victim tried to climb up the sides. It was bombarded, blinded and exhausted by the partially imbedded demon at the bottom. If foothold was gained at the top, the ant lion quickly writhed its way beneath the victim and produced a fresh slide. Few insects escaped from those pits and after being half buried and bitten by keen jaws, the softer parts were devoured. The shrivelled carcass was picked up on the ant lion's head and hurled out of the crater. The scattered remains brought inquisitive ants prowling in the vicinity of the fateful pits.

After a summer spent in this way the ant lion spun a silken cocoon deep in the sand. In this it was transformed and then it emerged as a creature with an elongated slender body, with four transparent wings, which reflected prismatic colors like Pompeiian glass in the sunlight—a fragile and beautiful flying thing with no hint of its rough vigor and cruelty in the larval stage.

The dragon fly and ant lion part of the lecture pleased the chief after he made several changes in expression which he called poetic.

This writing gave me an idea as to how I could become more useful in the department and have further breaks in the monotony of mounting specimens. I started a night course in stenography and typewriting, and after three weeks, with notebook on my knee and a batch of pencils sharpened on each end, sat in a front pew of St. Andrews Church in Harlem. When the staid pastor started his sermon, and noted my dashing pencil and the flipping of finished pages—the latter emphasized in the class as saving a split second—he gazed down upon me with a mingled look of surprise and concern. During the prayer, when I reverently stopped writing, I peeked at the pastor and ducked when I saw that he was peeking at me.

I told the chief about the accomplishment of taking down the sermon, but he wasn't much impressed. He said he would try dictating some letters when he had time, but didn't like the idea because it was too much like making a speech. That very night I was glad he had put it off, for in looking over the sermon, I was chagrined not to be able to read anything but scattered bits, which had no unity or coherence.

My typing, however, seemed more satisfactory. I could work with a finger of one hand and two of the other. I lugged an old machine up from the secretary's office but it was different from the one at school. The keys were so close-set they caught on my finger-nails in spite of my trimming them to the quick.

The chief wouldn't dictate, but wrote out some letters with a pencil and I tackled the machine.

He summed up the experiment by saying that he took as much time writing the letter with a pencil as he would writing a finished copy with ink, and that I took as much time rubbing out letters as tapping them in. "Besides," he concluded, "the clattering of that thing is awful."

In justice to stenographers, and to myself, who later engaged in professional shorthand, let me say that the novice at such endeavors can barely learn the rudiments in a few weeks' practice, no matter how determined he is.

And so ended the first year of my first job. My two weeks' vacation time arrived. I went to a country boarding-house in Connecticut, where there was milk every meal; but nothing exciting happened.

Arriving home on a late afternoon I was confronted

with bitter disappointment. The upper part of Quinn's Livery Stable had been burned out the night before, and I had missed the fire!

Strolling sadly about the vicinity I noticed the mounds of coke embers left in front of the fire hydrants. This meant that they had taken the horses off the engines and had pumped for several hours. I could visualize the heavy Amoskeag from 119th Street rocking on its springs as it put solidity into a hose line that one could stand on—and the others, some of the new nickle-plated engines. And I had missed it.

My dejection had not quite oozed out of my system when I returned the next morning to my work at the Museum. But something had cropped up. A series of articles on the local fauna was to be prepared. The chief was at work on his part of the program, his first paper being entitled, "The *Orthoptera* Found Within Fifty Miles of New York." The insect order of *Orthoptera* includes grasshoppers, crickets, walking sticks —and roaches. Of the lot the local grasshopper contingent is the most imposing, for there are over two dozen species.

Like all good scientific writers, he was concerned in preparing his "keys for identification."

His arrival at the curators' hour of ten was precise and precipitate.

"I have an idea," he snapped. "With the initial paragraph of each genus there will be a drawing of the metathorax—that is, of the grasshoppers. You said you could draw. Show me something with details."

I started to work at once. My particular pride was in shading cylindrical surfaces. Within an hour I had finished what I considered an excellent drawing of the 119th Street Amoskeag fire engine, showing the boiler details, and even the rivets being worked in. The shafts trailed on the ground since I was skeptical about my ability to draw horses.

Gratacap had come into the office and learned about the test. I walked through the arched door and laid the sketch before them.

The chief looked at the drawing, bent closer, then shouted to the high heavens.

"What on earth is this? I wanted a grasshopper!"

Red and confused, I explained that I had meant to delineate details, and tried to launch into the anatomy of a fire engine.

"Draw a grasshopper," was the order.

The jovial Gratacap shouted with laughter and pointed out that I had drawn many more spokes of wheels than the leg assembly of an orthopterous insect.

I requested permission to take a large specimen of the common *Acridium americanum* home that night, and bring back a pen and ink sketch in the morning.

That sketch was critically examined, analyzed through a reduction glass and passed as satisfactory. It went into the article, as did the series of my line drawings showing differentiation in the metathorax among grasshoppers.

The publication was formally issued and I received my first thrill in struggling toward science, for the article contained a line: "The figures in the text are by Mr. R. L. Ditmars."

The "Mr." was particularly gratifying and I proudly flourished it before my parents.

Chapter III

STRANGE PARTY OF THREE

My father walked slowly from my room. His hands were clasped behind him and he was gazing at the carpet. I could see that he was depressed.

We had been having a talk about my future. He had come in about a half hour before and found me absorbed in the catalogue of a company making fire engines. Another catalogue lay on the table.

"Where did you get these?" asked my father.

"From the Chief at the 119th Street Station. He just got the new ones and gave these to me."

I explained that the tendency was to design heavier apparatus, since buildings were becoming higher and there was talk of hauling with three horses instead of two, and that a heavier model of the La France Company was shown in the latest catalogue.

My father slipped through the pages and stopped at a full-page illustration of an ornate engine.

"That's a fine machine," I explained, "but getting old-fashioned. The boiler is sheathed in Russian iron, banded with brass. The stack is black with a brass calliope top. You can spot an Amoskeag blocks away. But her pumps are not heavy enough. They're beginning to shift those models to the outside districts."

My father stared at me keenly. "Tell me what some of these things mean," he said, pointing a finger here and there at the details of the engine.

"That," I said, "is the airdome, which is larger on a fire engine than on an ordinary pump owing to the speed of the pumping pistons."

"And this wheel on the side? It looks like the brake wheel of a freight car."

"That is one of the flywheels of the pumping mechanism; the two top cylinders drive the pistons of the two lower ones, which form the pump. But that type of wheel is passing out. La France is bringing out an engine with a smaller wheel, but much heavier rim."

The look on my father's face was easy to read. He was not keen about fire engines, but he was keen about my showing an interest in something he considered practical. I was sixteen and had tried to establish a collection of snakes; I had seemed to be keener about snakes than anything else, although my job was in the insect department of the American Museum of Natural History. My father, a practical business man, scorned the study of beetles and butterflies, but he appeared to have no fear of my wandering off as a professional butterfly hunter, since I talked too frequently of snakes. On this evening he saw a hopeful sign of a definite career for his son.

"I'll speak to Charles Xerfus. He has many business connections," said my father. "I'm convinced that with steady application and by beginning at the bottom, you would find a profession in one of these companies designing fire apparatus. As you say, buildings are getting taller and taller—cities are expanding."

"But, Pop," I almost wailed, "I don't want a job where they make fire engines, I'm only interested in them."

"What do you expect to make of yourself in years to come?"

"They'll start a reptile department at the Museum some day, but Mr. Jesup says I'm pretty young to plan on that now."

"Snakes, butterflies, fire engines and what were those two lectures you attended and were talking about for days—meteor—meteorology," my father snapped out the tongue-twisting word.

"You have too many interests, with not enough concentration to go ahead with any of them, except—" and I realized he was thinking about snakes.

It was at this point that he left the room.

My father's idea was that I pried into one interest after another and that so long as I did so, I couldn't hope to get anywhere. This book is an analysis of these successive pryings. I did not improve in later years. The disposition became more intensified and was the real foundation of my interest and happiness. Monotony, no matter where I have been, has never come near me. I think of my father with the utmost respect, but I am convinced that in my case, his analysis was wrong, although the reader may at times think otherwise. It was not long after the episode in my room that I had a demonstration of the varying interests of the matured scientific mind. It made a strong impression on me—for better or for worse only the future could tell.

My much-admired friend, Professor Smith, had received a small grant from his college to go to Florida on an insect-collecting trip and had invited me to accompany him as assistant. I made my way through a side street to the Clyde Line piers, lugging two satchels. As this was my first ocean trip, the *Arapahoe* looked big and impressive, although she would be considered a third-class coastal craft to-day.

The professor, an angular man between fifty and sixty, who was alternately restless and nervous or completely calm, was doing a sort of dance on the forward passenger deck.

"Raymond, go downstairs and find my trunk. I must look over my tubes and cyanide bottles."

The reason for the professor's disturbed state of mind was evident. Twin booms at the forward mast were clearing up a pile of trunks. The trunks were being loaded into a rope net for hoisting. The winchmen, standing behind the drums of two clattering machines on the lower deck, did perfect team work. One swung the loaded net into the air, the other used the set boom to pull the load inward. Then the first man dropped the load deep into the ship. Cues for hoisting, and the plunging descent were mere hand motions of a chief stevedore whose fingers curled upward as the signal to stop. Not a net-load of baggage appeared to receive a jolt. Each batch stopped just a few inches from the floor of the lower level, then gently settled. As the professor's trunk was not to be seen on the pier, it was evident that it had come aboard before he discovered the deft process of loading baggage, but he was not sure that his precious cases of bottles, cans and cork-lined boxes for pinning insects had been stopped by the mere flexing of a man's fingers.

The trunk, a big and battered affair, was discovered and carried by two protesting stewards to our cabin where it took up a third of the room, but made the professor happy as he rummaged through its contents and found them intact.

The adventure in Florida was to me like entering a new world. We worked through the Indian River district, then through cypress swamps—the latter fascinating with the buttressed bases of the trees, like the shoulders of great bottles, and the many "knees", like miniatures of church steeples. The season had been dry and there was little trouble in finding good footing through the swamps. The search was largely for butterfly and moth larvae. It was not the season to find co-

coons. We discussed previous cocoon hunting in the North, where islets of favorable bushes in the Jersey swamps, between the western base of the Palisades and Newark, could only be reached over the ice after a severe cold wave in winter, when we made our way through a sea of dead cat-tails, watching for thin spots where there was moving water. These vast and rather spectral swamps of Florida were much easier to traverse and less dangerous. I saw few reptiles. The lacy, but interweaving, foliage overhead produced an all-day shade. The muddy, reddish soil absorbed the light. On the lower vegetation the professor found abundant material, which he "pickled" in tubes of preserving fluid. I marvelled at his botanical knowledge, for there never was a bush or plant from which he collected a specimen that he did not name without hesitation and enter among the data in his note-book.

It was about this time that I started to sense the versatility of Professor Smith, whom I had previously met only at scientific meetings where I had assisted him in arranging boxes of specimens to illustrate his papers.

After an early morning start we came to an embankment of the Southern Railroad. Hearing a train, we waited before climbing and crossing. The train roared by with what seemed to me quite a normal sound, but I noticed the professor beating time in twos with his forefinger to attract my attention, as the two-wheeler trucks ran over a joint. We were soon on the top of the embankment and the professor pointed to a quarter-inch gap between the rails.

"It was very cool last night," he said. "Notice how these rails contracted. They will be squeezed tight together when this roadbed heats up by noontime and——"

The remark was interrupted by a rush over gravel and cinders and a sweep of his small net. Whatever he had seen was captured, as the net was deftly turned over, but the momentum carried the victor down the embankment where he landed in a cloud of dust among abandoned railroad ties.

Breaking into my startled query as to whether he was hurt came his request for a bottle. He had no thought of bruises, for he had captured a rare species of *Cicindela* or tiger beetle. These are small creatures, less than an inch long, that run swiftly in open places and take to the wing when pursued. They are of iridescent shades of vivid green or red, and, as I pulled a bottle from the bag suspended from my shoulder-strap and the specimen was plopped inside, it gleamed like an emerald that might adorn a necklace. We were elated by capturing a dozen more; then we looked for a spot to leave the embankment and enter the swamp on the other side. Firm patches indicated good footing.

Before leaving the track, however, the entomologist took pains to point to a thin cable plated across the inner edge of the rails.

"That compensates for the gap when the metal is

contracted," he remarked, in a lecture-room tone, "and makes a continuous line of the rail for transmission of electric signals—the continuously coupled rail being the carrier."

I concluded that since railroad beds were good places to collect beetles, the professor had observed such details incidentally, but my deduction was wrong.

Our operations led to the Everglades which were, to me, the gateway to the Paradise of the serpent world. I considered the possible establishment of a serpent collection in the attic of the Museum. Such utterly innocent creatures as yellow-ringed king snakes, carmine-blotched corn snakes and tan chicken snakes were bagged as my trophies. Water moccasins, which slithered into the pickerel weed, were reluctantly permitted to go their way, since they were poisonous. To me, they were highly attractive and interesting, but there was no alibi for them as to character. Even at that, I viewed the bags of my innocuous captives with considerable doubt. Their bulk and numbers were highly formidable, as introductions to the idea of "study specimens."

One particularly momentous day, we started out after a careful checking of accessories. We were writhing our way through scrub palmetto and thorny bushes when the professor stopped, peered at a leaf, then changed his spectacles for a pair that glittered like ground crystal at the rims.

"Hah-h-h, it is here," he exclaimed.

Coming close to him and gazing at the leaf, I saw

an insect slightly larger than a mosquito. It looked like a wasp, reduced to miniature.

"I thought so!" he said, and called for a small cyanide or poison-fume bottle, which was cautiously placed over the leaf and the narcotized midget dropped into the bottle. A scientific name, many times the length of the captive, was written on a slip of paper, the locality was appended and the data dropped into the jar.

He directed a long forefinger at the fragile specimen, its limbs entangled in the layer of cotton overlying the cyanide stratum at the bottom, and informed me that this midget was a parasite, imbedding its eggs in the larvae of insects destructive to the fruit groves of Florida.

"Parasitology," declared Professor Smith, "is a great field open to entomologists. Here are man's allies, far more powerful in their intensive action than sprays and poisons. They should be cultivated and their respective kinds spread broadcast in infected areas."

His foresight and the practicability of his later research has been dramatically demonstrated by his work and that of other government entomologists.

During the Everglades reconnoiter, there was an incident that stands out as one of the high spots in my early life.

We were in a hammock, which is a sort of island of slightly elevated land in the swamp. The ground was firm; and there was a growth of small cypress and gum trees. There was also some dwarf palmetto, looking like palm-leaf fans radially protruding from rough knobs. We had stopped for lunch, and our preparations were simple. We carried the professor's invariable selection which I have found to be an ideal midday meal in hot country. Each of us had slung from his belt two wrapped slices of bread, cut the length of the loaf. Besides this, each of us carried a can of tomatoes. All we had to do was to cut off the top of the can, heat the contents, and spread it on the bread. After a diet like this one can walk for hours without getting thirsty—at least anyone who takes kindly to hot country.

We were seated on a fallen trunk of cypress, in a litter of live and dead ground palmetto, and, as assistant, I was opening the tomato cans with a jack knife. As I walked around gathering stems and sticks to make a little fire to heat them, I heard a sound like that produced by making a circle of the mouth and drawing in air. It was followed by the sharp buzz of a rattlesnake.

Swinging toward the sound, my eyes were riveted upon what was up to that time the most thrilling spectacle of my life. Coiled in an open patch was a diamond-back rattler, its body a full three inches in diameter and its head as broad as a man's hand. The professor, hearing the sharp sound, came over.

"A beautiful creature!" he exclaimed.

I was between the devil and the deep blue sea. I should have liked to attempt the capture of that rattler, but I knew full well that I would have no place to keep him and that his arrival in the North would be regarded

Edge of a Florida cypress swamp where the Professor led the author toward a strange adventure.

Diamond-back rattler. A thrilling actor when encountered deep in the southern wilds.

In the desert adventure the hornless "horned toads" were extremely difficult to detect.

A typical horned "toad." Nature has seen fit to provide spines among desert lizards, either on parts of them or bristling all over.

with horror. The professor realized the situation and suggested that in time to come I could harbor such specimens without difficulty—and that, under the present circumstances, we make it a three party group and start our luncheon.

Possibly no stranger outdoor party ever gathered. The rattler's neck was arched and he regarded us intently. The buzz of the rattle was at first incessant. As we consumed the last elongated slice of bread, the buzzing died down and then was no more than an occasional flick of the warning appendage. But there was not a move on the professor's part or on mine but what the broad head, with its gleaming eyes, was directed toward one or the other of us.

When I say that it was a strange trio I am recalling the conversation of the entomologist, a scientist internationally recognized for his elaborate monographs, his discoveries of new species and the respect of his students for his methods in teaching; yet here he was talking about subjects remote from entomology. He discussed the character of soils and deplored the thought that some day there would be canals dug across the Everglades. The area we had traversed, he insisted, was composed of a stratum of soil of but moderate depth, beneath which was coral. Moreover, the soil was impregnated with sphagnum moss and vegetable debris. Plant life had struggled to become adapted.

"If they drain it for farming and those areas become dry and take fire, they will burn like Irish peat, and what is left will be little better than a desert," he insisted.

His predictions have been amply borne out, to the sorrow of Florida.

His discussion of soils was but the beginning of our noonday talk, for, to my surprise, he branched into a discussion of the evolution of steam vessels from the side-wheeler to propeller type. He talked of developments and improvements, of steam applied to fighting vessels during the Civil War, and described the specifications of the *Hartford, Brooklyn, Harriet Lane,* and *Powatan.* These names I distinctly remember.

"These engines were rather crude," he continued, "their attachments on wooden supports. When we return I wish to see the engine of our steamer and note the use of triple expansion. Practical observation is much better than reading from books."

Glancing upward, he broke into his discussion by saying that there appeared to be a storm in the Gulf and our work would be interrupted by heavy rain. Here was a thrill for me: the mention of weather. I was eager to discuss this with him and told him that I intended to make a study of weather, that I had noticed that streaky clouds in winter meant more in indicating approaching storms than at other times of the year.

He talked at length of cloud classification as I had heard it discussed in lectures at the Museum. In the formal tone of the classroom, he held me spellbound and a little embarrassed by his reciprocal interest.

And all this time, the group included a man, a boy and a big rattlesnake. The latter was the first to leave the party—and it was time we broke up and went to work. The symmetrical coil shifted, then all parts started to move. A six-foot, sage-green body, with chain of diamond markings, straightened and glided toward a low tangle.

"A beautiful creature," reiterated the professor.

In our cabin, with mosquitoes humming outside the draped white cloth over my cot, I thought rapidly before sleep could blot things out. About the three of us—the professor and me and the big rattler; my bags with the king, corn and chicken snakes, the *Brooklyn*, *Hartford*, *Harriet Lane* and—soils of Florida. The professor could classify clouds and was a botanist who had achieved wide fame. I was interested in fire engines, but, then again, I was determined to study snakes. The scene of my father leaving my room had shocked me. I was working in an entomological department, but I wasn't going to be an entomologist. The professor was snoring, very lightly. He was a distinguished man. Would I ever be? Where was I bound for—but he was a big man and read about steamboats, maybe—yes he, when he was my age——

Chapter IV

TANGENTS

The influence of Professor Smith was strong, his versatility inspiring. He had fanned a flame of inquisitiveness, and unconsciously steered me toward prying into the "why" of things, which developed into widely diversified studies. My father relaxed to a grim smile of watchfulness; but I thought I detected a gleam of approval. What is to come will show whether or not his worst fears concerning the vacillating interests of his son were to be realized.

My family had relinquished its restraint and permitted me to acquire a collection of snakes.

How was it possible to become an expert by watching snakes in glass-fronted boxes? How did I first know what to feed them—how to treat them? There was little to be learned from books in those days, except points about classification.

If one is strongly interested in a subject, usually intuition helps out. I remember that I sensed what new kinds of specimens would accept as food—and the feeding of snakes is very different from the care of other vertebrates. Some snakes will eat only warm-blooded prey, such as rodents and birds; others nothing but cold-blooded quarry like frogs and fish. A few will take both cold- and warm-blooded food, but are particular as to the size and kind of their victims. Some are cannibalistic, but will eat only certain kinds of snakes; quite a few feed upon lizards; and some species are insectivorous. Many snakes, provided with the proper food, feed readily, while others are nervous and will not feed if they are in any way disturbed, even though the disturbance comes hours before food is offered them. A few species cannot be induced to feed in captivity.

Those were the problems that came along with the development of my collection. But there was usually something about the looks of a snake, or its indicated relationship to specimens in the collection that led me to offer it food which would be accepted. Sometimes the hunch went wrong. I remember some small specimens that would eat nothing but snails and some fair-sized ones that would touch nothing but smooth-scaled lizards and nearly starved before I hit upon the diet they required.

The shedding of a snake's skin is like a holiday in its life, and inability to cast the skin may bring the speedy end of the reptile. Watching for that process and furthering it seemed to come natural to me in my early care of the collection. I noticed carefully the condition of the eyes of my specimens since the cap-like covering is also cast and becomes blue, like a bubble filled with smoke, a week or more before the shedding. About forty-eight hours before casting—longer with some species, shorter with others—the eyes clear, because of an aqueous film which forms under the skin and loosens it. After this happens the serpent should crawl from its old integument. If it doesn't, and the mysteriously appearing film dries up, the skin may tighten, become hard and encase the body. With captives, there are always a few that must be bathed and divested of their old clothing. Then there are maladies of the mouth, of the delicate skin between the scales, or internal parasites with which to contend. Docile and temperamental kinds must be treated very differently. With the latter I had considerable success, breeding three generations of one poisonous species. Elimination of the shock of capture means much with the temperamental kinds. I recall sitting like a statue on the floor for half an hour with aching joints, while a diamond rattlesnake alternately turned its head toward me, then inspected a dead rabbit—which he finally gulped down.

I was about twenty-one when I took over the new and empty Reptile House at the Zoölogical Park, donated my own collection, then brought together specimens from all over the world. Here were broad opportunities for delving into the wants of species I had never heard about except in terms of scale counts, or the like, in scientific books.

With a task like this it might seem that I was destined to think of little else, but a new line of thought came to me one afternoon at the Park. It was during a post mortem. A python had died and it was to be carefully examined by Dr. Harlow Brooks, who served as visiting pathologist to the collections of the New York Zoölogical Society. I greatly admired this brilliant young doctor who had an affable way of conducting his work. His assistant, Thomas Deacon, made the preliminary incision after the twenty-foot reptile had been placed on its back and bent in hairpin form on the long dissecting table. Deacon made a small opening in the hide; then with heavy scissors, the lower jaw with a ball-point, he cut the skin the entire length of the reptile—to the base of the tail. The object of the ball-pointed scissors was to avoid damage to the viscera. With the body opened, Deacon stood back while Dr. Brooks made his preliminary inspection. Nothing abnormal was evident on the outside surface of the viscera.

Next came the removal of various units of the anatomy, which were separately placed on the table. With smaller, ball-tipped scissors the doctor laid open the respiratory tract, bent closer, beckoned for me to do likewise, and disclosed the cause of the python's death. Closely scattered along the passages were whitish nodules with necrotic margins.

"That's strange," said Dr. Brooks, "those lesions look like tuberculosis, but I have never heard of it before among reptiles."

Deacon was sent for some test tubes containing culture medium in which germs might be propagated. Some of the nodules were removed for thin slicing by the microtome, then for examination under the microscope.

"The trouble," explained the doctor, "in looking for the 'bugs' that started this, is that they are likely to be so mixed with other bacteria that have invaded the lesions that they are hard to differentiate or isolate."

He rubbed a probe around the nodules, then plunged it into the jelly-like culture solution in the test tubes.

"We'll try to grow some of these 'bugs,' " he said.

Deacon casually put the tubes in his vest-pocket until there was a chance to place them in the culture oven.

It was then that I decided it was high time to take up the study of bacteriology, the science of germs.

After buying the classic and bulky work of Delafield and Prudden and reveling in its circled illustrations giving microscopic delineation of tiny organisms, I found that the references in this book led me to many other books whose cost was shocking; but gradually I accumulated a fair library.

In my microscopical work, Tommy Deacon lent generous aid. He had instruments and full equipment in the Park's laboratory. There was a thrill in looking at the most devilish kinds of disease-producing organisms through the powerful oil-immersion lens. Where on earth Tommy put a hand on the slides I don't know, but he produced specimens of anthrax, tetanus, typhoid and similarly formidable types. We searched for a slide of Asiatic cholera, but couldn't find it. I remember my great pride when a downtown laboratory worker whom I visited gave me the chance of personally making up a slide of one of the most wicked of pus-producing bacteria—a streptococcus that attaches in chains. I brought back the slide, the strings of germs properly stained with methylene blue and showed it to Tommy.

"Pretty," he said. "That's pretty."

The studies advanced until I knew well the significance and effects of the germs of infection, some far more dangerous than others, and realized the full horror of a streptococcus infection which appeared after laceration of my left forearm, and caused me weeks of agony as well as nearly incapacitating my arm.

My studies of bacteriology were sharply criticized as inconsistent. They extended over months until I finished the more intensive work, with the satisfied thought that here was a subject I could read about with understanding as the science advanced—as advanced it has, to bring great benefit both to humanity and to domestic animals. In later years, the knowledge stood by me in my research work of clarifying the action of snake poisons attended by the destruction of tissue by certain kinds of micro-organisms. One of the highest points in my appreciation of the significance of bacteriology came during my contacts with Noguchi, as we worked on snake poison. He delighted in dealing with complex problems of disease-germ contact in various parts of the world. When he found that I had read his papers, and that I wanted further explanation, and clearly knew what I was talking about, we became close friends. He outlined some astonishing theories which he was checking in relation to tropical diseases. Unfortunately, his busy life prevented him from making some of the investigations he had planned. I shall always think of this quiet man as one of the world's greatest benefactors.

I had an uneasy feeling that I had been reading many books, but had made no showing with one of my own, so I started my book on the reptiles of North America, determined to produce for the first time a book in readable terms which should be at the same time a thorough diagnosis and identification work on all the known species of snakes, lizards, turtles and crocodilians of North America, with appended habits of many of them. This task divided itself into two parts—the preparation of photographs for the plates, and the writing of the text which I estimated would come to about a quarter of a million words, and take approximately two years.

On the dining-room table of my small apartment the accumulating manuscript built up higher and higher. The room was illuminated by a gas mantle. Books were stacked on chairs and a buffet which served as my working library. The top shelf carried rows of bottles of pickled snakes and lizards. When it was necessary to count scale rows and make measurements, the room reeked with alcohol. My young wife kept me company by sleeping in a rocker in the midst of the litter, except when she went into the bedroom to look after the baby. The writing was started after we had cleared the dinner table and together had washed and wiped the dishes. It continued past midnight. Occasionally, I turned from writing to the photographic work, adding new species that came in. There were over fifteen hundred plates from which over four hundred were finally selected for the book. Most of the photography was done at the Park. I carried on the development of the plates in the bathroom at home, pungent with the fumes of a kerosene red-light.

There were diversions, for I had resumed my study of the weather—which continues to this day. Then again, friends dropped in, usually at inopportune moments when pickled snakes reposed on their backs in soup plates or on the serving platter. Of course it was disturbing to drop a job like that, to calm down and be sociable. But I dropped the specimens into their respective jars, put tabulations of scale counts under a paper weight, opened the windows to let out the alcohol fumes, and heaved a sigh as I assumed the rôle of host. Thoughts reverted to those rows of bottles.

It may be of interest to step out of that picture for a moment and see what happened to the book.

To my pride, it became a standard in its field, and was printed in many editions. Two years ago it was decided that I should revise it, to bring it up-to-date.

Many new species had been named in the thirty years since the book had first appeared. Moreover, it was necessary to write in a wealth of new habits, and to arrange new keys for identification.

I did the job of rewriting in my modern research laboratory, a room fifty feet long. The photographic lights were run into the prop alcoves and extra shelves were built for books and bottles. There was a ten-foot writing table on which to spread out the manuscript, notes and check lists. Every facility for a job of the kind was at hand. Into this atmosphere came my wife and asked how I was getting along. She gazed around the laboratory.

"Quite a difference from the old dining-room table," she remarked. Her implication was that this would be a much better book; that here, with a background of switchboards and wall plugs, the photography should be a more finished product than my early efforts at home. But what I told her made us both happy. The early job had been carefully done; the book would be no better, relatively speaking. It would be up-to-date, with changes in scientific names; it would include many new species and new observations, but the old plates would be used as they stood. While I realized the incongruity of speaking this way, in a thoroughly equipped establishment—I told her that those old sunlight photographs and bathroom-developed plates could not be better; that this modern equipment was for speed and could not improve on the quality of the plodding, old-fashioned work so painstakingly done.

But to go back to the first writing of that book.

I have mentioned occasional diversions. There was one that stands out; it necessitated another course of study in the midst of my writing.

My wife and I decided that we wanted to own an automobile. The desire was formulated long before we could get one. Short stops for magazine writing, while I plugged on the book, finally built up a fund, and a car was bought. It was a brute of a thing with a very chuggy engine, but in those days we took pride in motor noise. The doubtful point about our purchase was, that though it looked spick and span with the brass shined up, it was still cantankerous. Its previous owner had said it had received a bit of service, but I was suspicious that he had not been modest in this assertion. At any rate, I was afraid to trust it on trips longer than a few blocks from the garage. We had a conference and it was decided that I must give up two evenings a week to attend a night school offering a course in gasoline engine construction and manipulation. The beginning of the course was encouraging. The very first night I came home with a chart showing the working parts of an automobile. I removed the pictures from one of the dining-room walls and fastened up the chart with thumb tacks. It took up the greater part of the wall. With the chart on one side and the pickled snakes on the other, all domestic atmosphere vanished, but what was the use of worrying about the impression on guests while we were so busy? The school also furnished a can of gritty soap. I felt this was a clever idea on their part to induce the pupil to come back, since it took about two days to get rid of the grime from an evening's instruction. The course lasted a number of weeks. I received a diploma, but so did everyone else in the class.

The car's trips were lengthened. One evening we ran from the Bronx to Getty Square in Yonkers. On the way up, the engine did some strange stunts that had not been even remotely hinted at in the class. I tried in various ways to put it in order and finally the motor ran smoothly again. Possibly all it had needed was to cool off. At any rate, I took the next afternoon off and dissected the engine. It was utterly different from any of the demonstrator motors in the class. I found some valves that needed grinding, the magneto was off time and the breaker points pitted. Word had been left at the house that I would be back for dinner. I didn't get the motor assembled and running again until past midnight, and I returned in such a state of grime that I used a whole can of the gritty soap, now constantly associated with my automobile activities.

The big day arrived when we left for a Sullivan County boarding-house from which I could wander out to a rattlesnake ledge that was my personal secret. It seemed fine to roll away in our own chugging conveyance instead of boarding an Ontario and Western train and buying our lunch at Middletown—allegedly homemade sandwiches wrapped in glazed paper.

The trip was successful, except for the final lap. Bound homeward with the running boards heaped high with baggage and cans of special oil for the motor, we had got to within fifty miles of the Bronx when I struck one of those dreaded board signs called by early motorists a "deetoor."

The engine had never faltered, although it had boiled intermittently. In negotiating an atrocious back road, however, something went terribly wrong with the transmission. There was a crunch which made the car shudder, then a noise from the intermediate gear which sounded as if the vehicle was about to burst in the middle. Fortunately, I was alone in the front, except for a bag of rattlers, and could quickly pry up the floorboards. After the greasy job of removing the transmission-plate and digging away a jelly-like mass that hid the gears, I decided that a tooth had been stripped from the second speed and, getting among its interlocking neighbors, had churned them into bits. This meant that an important part of the gear mechanism could not be used, but I might be able to speed up the car on low gear and then drop into high. It was worth trying, but first I removed the draining plug at the bottom of the gear case to allow the grease and broken teeth to flow out, and so save other gears from the chewing process. A large, viscid puddle formed under the car; then I tried starting from low into high.

The clutches in those days meant business. They grabbed with sudden and titanic force. The car leaped forward as if shot from a catapult. The plan was not a success. My wife regained her seat and looked worried.

I told her I was only trying something. I was overwhelmed with responsibility and embarrassment. I remembered the impressive chart on the dining-room wall and the nights at the automobile school. To have said I had taken a course on engines would have made a poor alibi. We had spent money to enable me to diagnose ailments of an automobile.

Telling my wife that I would return in a few minutes I walked back along the road. I had an idea, but it was not backed by much confidence.

A short time before we had passed a small Italian shop with open boxes of spaghetti in the window. It seemed much farther back than I had thought, but I finally reached it and inquired if they kept cans of olive oil. The reply was vociferous. They had olive oil and it was the genuine, imported product. I bought four pint cans.

Returning to the car, I poured a pint around the edge of the leather-faced clutch, which in this early type of car ran in the open without pretense of encasement, and was the diameter of a dishpan. Trying the low to high starting again I was thrilled. The engine raced but the car gathered momentum and we went on. My attitude was calm, as if such matters were but a phase of night-school instruction. During some of our stops homeward the bucking tendency returned, but more oil calmed it down.

My nerves were at a stage of extreme tension when we arrived home and I made numerous trips upstairs to clean out the car. Fortunately, it was almost a coast down to the garage. When the car had shuddered into its berth with its back against the wall, I took a last look at the clutch, or rather, what remained of it—some shreds of burned leather drooping around the flywheel. I related my experiences to the garage proprietor. He was not impressed with my mechanical knowledge.

"We'll get to it in the morning," he said. "We'll have to drop the propeller shaft, take out the transmission and remove the clutch mechanism."

He spoke in tones of dismissal, but hinted at a sizable bill. However, the depressing effect of his attitude faded out when my wife congratulated me after I reached home. She was sitting up, bright-eyed, waiting to talk about the trip.

"It's lucky you took that course at the automobile school," was her greeting.

The book was done, the proof was read, and a car was gnawing at our income. Something had to be done.

Writing for magazines had used up most of my notes on material which could be made popular. There was the lecture field, but, with me, it had hitherto been limited to talks on snakes, and circularization among prospective places brought poor response. It looked as though there were a lot of people who didn't like snakes. But the idea of lecturing persisted; it would be a change from writing. There followed, however, an interim during which, aside from my daily duties as a curator of reptiles, I did little but ponder over a renewal of outside activities.

The solution came during a visit to one of the libraries when I discovered a bulky and faded volume of Harper's "Pictorial History of the Civil War." I spent hours with it, until finally an attendant tapped me on the shoulder and told me that the library was closing. It left pictures in my mind of such fighting steam vessels as the *Hartford*, the *Harriet Lane* and the *Powatan*. Where had I heard those names? Oh, yes, from Professor Smith. I delved into the text relating to the opening of the war, the first two years of disastrous results for the North, Bull Run, the Peninsula Campaign, Fredericksburg and Chancellorsville. The details were fascinating, and I remembered that, when I was studying history in school, I had turned back to read about those very battles, briefly described. Professor Stevens of Barnard had said, "There is a boy who has absorbed American history because he likes it"—a gratifying remark compared to some of the comments on my other studies. But why had I liked to think of those battles? My father had inspired my enthusiasm. A major in the Confederate Army—the aide-de-camp of Lee—the thought of Lee had guided him in giving me a middle name.

I went back to the library for further reading, and in books and documents I learned that the government had an extensive collection of old photographic negatives of the Civil War. The die was cast. There was my lecture work—a series of lectures connected with the Civil War, if I could get permission to make lantern slides from those government plates.

My wife received the new idea with reservation. Another course of study! I was afraid she would criticize it, but she didn't.

Having received letters from President Roosevelt about reptiles and answering them in a way that seemed to satisfy him, I obtained leave to go to Washington to see the President with a plea to make a series of lantern slides from the plates and arrange lectures commemorating notable fifty-year anniversaries of the war.

The President was surprised at the request and asked questions about my plans for the lectures. I outlined a program which interested and pleased him. He felt that such lectures on American history were needed, and granted me permission to make the slides.

A young army officer was assigned to help in selecting the negative plates. The portion of the photographic department of the War College allotted to these plates looked like a glazier's shop. The plates were in racks and ranged from close to twenty inches in length to about four by five inches in size. All of them had been prepared under the old "wet plate" process and were saffron yellow in color.

"You slide them out and look 'em over," said the officer. "If I dropped one my heart would stop."

I selected three hundred from which prints were made, the clarity of which could not have been excelled by modern methods. From these prints the lantern slides were produced. The prints were mounted for me in an album by a government technician and that album is one of my most cherished possessions. The government gave me only a modest bill for the actual cost of the work.

The research involved in preparing the lectures was very carefully done, and culminated in another trip to Washington to go through the files and make notes on the colors of uniforms of regiments, gun carriages, supply wagons and ambulances. The slides were turned over to an artist for coloring. The cost used up our spare money but quickly turned out to be a good and lasting investment. The lectures received much commendation.

My first Civil War lecture was held in the Sixty-Ninth Regiment Armory, before the regiment and its guests during a memorial commemorating the first battle of Bull Run. Among the lantern slides were photographs of the Sixty-Ninth, the Colonel, Michael Corcoran, and other detachments of the impressive Federal columns that moved to the first field of battle.

The preparations for that lecture were elaborate. The screen for the projection of the pictures was the largest that had been erected in the city. Two theatrical electricians fed the fifty-ampere arcs of special stage stereopticans, and after their labors, they looked as if they had crawled from a coal-hole. The immense and brilliantly illuminated pictures were received with prolonged applause and, to add to the volume of sound, James Mullens, drum major of the Sixty-Ninth, had his block of field music drawn up at one side, and when scenes of the regiment flashed on the screen, gave the signal for long ruffles or a fanfare from the buglers. They had built me a high platform in the center of the Armory from which to speak. I was instructed to speak slowly and loud. I did this and was gratified to hear the ring of my voice reverberating from the ceiling girders —but I was hoarse for a week.

But above thoughts of the war lectures was my concern with something which happened in 1912 connected with my father who, as I have said, had been a major in the Confederate service. August was approaching— the fiftieth anniversary of the second battle of Bull Run, a high spot among Confederate victories. I visited my father, who still insisted on activity in business, and told him he was to take a week's vacation, that I had arranged everything and that we were going to visit the battlefield of Bull Run on the date of the fiftieth anniversary of combat; that I had drawn an extensive chart of the field and we would go over the old ground.

By way of Washington we arrived at Manassas, Virginia, where I hired a horse and buggy. My father was like a boy out of school. On the heights near Groveton we looked down on an arena of beautiful country where one hundred thousand soldiers of the opposing armies had fought it out. My chart lay open on the grass.

"There was a Federal battery of rifled guns on that

hill," I remarked. "They were using conoidal shells and their fire was very damaging to your columns converging along the roads."

"We were forming in those meadows," snapped my father, with the glow of remembrance in his eyes. "There was heavy artillery fire from that other side."

"Yes," I pointed to the chart, "Pope had lined up batteries there. You were getting a direct fire from smooth-bores—canister, probably. Those expensive new guns on the hill wouldn't use grape or canister which would dull the lands of their rifling; they were swell guns for those days."

My father straightened, he seemed to grow larger as he surveyed the field, which rolled in long billows like a golf park.

"They were coming over those knolls," he said, "with a swarm of skirmishers ahead of them. The meadows smoked with the skirmish fire behind which was wave after wave of troops stretching out as far as you could see. They dropped and lay prone and more troops were coming. They were feeding in from the back roads. We could hear their drums. That was an idea of Pope's—field music up to the time of deploying for action.

"I was on that knoll," he pointed to a grassy hill at the side. "General Pryor sent an order for several batteries. They came at a gallop and were firing a moment after the trails were dropped. I heard the orders—'canister, double-charge.' "

A breeze picked up my chart and blew it closed, as if it were a weak part of the picture.

"Our enfilading fire into those lines started turmoil. They were on their feet and falling back, their alignment was gone and toward this disorder we plunged. We drove them back a couple of miles. It was the end of Pope's plans and his campaign."

I put a stone on the fluttering chart. The narrator waved a hand at it as if to dismiss its cold delineation.

"And those crack rifled guns," he continued sarcastically, "—we had them and equipment that took us a week to list."

In a little inn near Manassas Junction we put up for the night. We were coated with red dust which had streaked our hands and faces, because of the heat of the day. On those Virginia roads the fine dust spurted from beneath one's feet.

"Tired?" I asked my father, as I looked for an extra chair on which to stretch my aching feet after all the hiking.

"Not much," came the answer, as my father gazed out of a window. "We'll work along the Warrenton Pike tomorrow."

A phase of that historical research has remained with me to the present. I am keen both on wandering over old battlefields and on hunting snakes, and not long ago I recommended to some brother scientists the naming of a new subspecies of rattlesnake which I had captured in the path of Sherman's march to the sea.

Chapter V

DIAMOND-BACKS

Two pictures recurred again and again to my mind during a desperate illness. Through interminable weeks of dressings and bandages when a glance at my arm or leg was a study in bone outlines, I built up two images of places I wanted to go when I got well. Out of a haze of places and spots, these two took form so that I could visualize even the colors of the surroundings. One was a definite spot; the other offered more ground for wandering. The spot was the base of a huge pine in Florida whose roots radiated in all directions. Some were as big as the trunks of fair-sized trees. For twenty feet or more from their fusion with the base they were largely, or partially, bare, and between their undulations were holes and hollows. It was clear that beneath this radiating mass was an underground chamber, like a great inverted plate, bedded with pine needles that had sifted in from the carpeting which surrounded the tree on all sides and which saturated the air with fragrance at noon. That was fine bedding for the serpent clan.

That flat, underground chamber was, in my thoughts,

the home or den of a colony of diamond-back rattle-snakes, king species of all the rattlers, and growing to be eight feet or more in length. That they sheltered there, in partial hibernation during the mild winters of Florida, I had no doubt. And that a fair number made this their home during the prowling season after preying upon cotton-tail rabbits and quail, I felt was probable. Also, here was an ideal spot for the mother rattler to retire and await the birth of her six to a dozen foot-long babies.

What had brought to my mind this particular spot and the yearning to go there? I had seen it for five minutes during my trip with Professor Smith. Thunder was rumbling and we were making our way out of the pines to get to our horse and ramshackle cart.

"Hurry," urged the professor, "the horse may be frightened and break loose."

I had hesitated among that tangle of roots and holes —and picked up a segment broken from a rattle. We had left for the North a few days later with no chance to return to the tree.

I outlined all of this to my nurse.

Her glance was conciliating.

"When you get out of here," she said, "you are going to take a trip to Nova Scotia, where it is restful and cool."

Here was another of the sort of suggestions I had been getting on and off for years. Nova Scotia, where the only reptiles were a few turtles and garter snakes. No, my way led south—and that is the way my life has been, mainly toward hot countries—although, inconsistently, I am fond of winter in my home area.

The night nurse was more sympathetic. At least she listened to what I said without offering advice. She asked if she could read to me and I referred her to a government publication on the origin of cyclonic storms! Her voice droned on and faltered. With an effort I turned and saw that she was asleep.

A second picture of a place to go, when emancipation from pain and tedium came to an end, had risen in my mind. The dim light and the nodding nurse faded out. Yes, another place, but not a particular spot. I had sensed it but never seen it or been within a thousand miles of it—the western slope of the Sierra Nevada, in California, the coniferous forests, again pines, but many pines. There lay the trunks of great trees that had fallen and from which the bark had loosened. I was stripping bark in search of the most beautiful snake in North America, the coral king. It is secretive and rare, and what a find! A yard is its maximum length. To my imagination, finding one hiding would be like discovering a handsome necklace. The scales glow like enamel in rings of scarlet, yellow and black. Yes, California, but that would come later. It took money to go to California. It was easier to get to Florida, to the big pine with its spreading roots, its holes and hollows. The two visions were equally alluring. A cool sheet fluttered under my chin—the nurse must be awake—I would dream away this monotony in thoughts of the big pine and——

The Clyde liner slowly swung into the dock at Jacksonville. All around was flat country, low river vegetation and the silhouettes of a few palms; but I knew that a journey southward would take me to a little settlement from which a buckboard ride would bring me to the edge of pine forest and the infiltrating swamp where my tree stood. It was early spring and chilly. Waking the next morning in the settlement, I found fern ice in the washtub outside the cabin. Just a skim to be gone when the sun was up, but I was sure that my tree, if I found it, would have no populace at its doors. Nevertheless, I must find the tree. I was soon on my way, with canvas bags at my belt and grit cakes wrapped in greasy paper as a lunch.

Toward midday I had moments of disappointment. The pine forest stretched on monotonously. No tree stood out. I retraced my way along a "run," then crossed and located another "run"—indentations that were waterways during heavy rains. Where was my pictured vision of that spot? I felt that I must have gone around and around it, but, as I started back in dejection, it suddenly faced me. I still remember my indrawn breath of realization. In a solitude undisturbed by human trails stood the pine. Its outflung roots made it distinctive. Here was a spot I would hold secret. If some of its denizens went away with me, they would be only a few. I wanted to remember that tree as a spot where the clan continued to lurk in shelter.

There was no life in sight among the nestling hollows of the roots, but I found something to show that the trail was warm. Laced among fibrous tendrils at the surface, then extending downward and turning out of sight, were fragments of a cast skin disintegrated by ants and dampness. The lateral scales were as large as my small finger nail.

"A diamond-back," I said to myself, "and a big one."

That first day was the partial realization of my dream. I let the old horse jog along back to the little settlement with empty bags. The day was nearly gone—an eventful day, though nothing had happened except the proof that something I had visioned was really there. I arrived at the cabin in time to hear the sizzling of bacon and grit cakes, which the cadaverous whites of that area appear to live on throughout the year. But the greasy meal tasted good—it was different. I was hoping for a warm spring day, when heat on the pine needles would bring out the sweet odor of the forest floor—and bring out, too, the colony that sheltered beneath the tree.

It came in a few days, with a breeze from the southwest, sweeping warm air across Florida off the tropic waters of the Gulf. And again I started the trip to the tree, with rolled-up bags in my belt and a greasy package of fried grit cakes. I tried to get a can of tomatoes, remembering the professor's favorite fare; but there was none at the cabin, and the little general store was three miles off my route. At any rate, I was too excited to bother about eating, except to think, as the lanky horse jogged along, about the miserable fare among these backwoods whites, who looked more bony than the horse.

Driving into the pines as far as I could, I unhitched, tied the horse and trudged on. I had no trouble in locating the tree this time—just a bit of manoeuvering. The direction of the "runs" guided me and at last I saw the pine a bit ahead. Being of greater diameter than others of the forest, it stood out in unmistakable boldness.

A thrill of anticipation stopped me a hundred yards away. Were they there, or not? Had the clan come out to coil and bask among those great roots? Close to the sheltering holes, they would try to go back in if I approached too quickly. So I stood where I was and figured out just what I would do if they were there. To edge a big diamond-back into a canvas bag would be no easy matter. I didn't relish grasping one of those powerful brutes by the neck and dropping it into the bag. A six-foot thrashing rattler with a weight of ten or twelve pounds is an adversary to be respected. Its fangs are an inch long and it can twist its head from side to side. Pine needles are a slippery floor upon which to pin down such a head while one's fingers creep up on the neck. I remembered a stirring tussle with a big timber rattler in the North, a third the diameter and power of a grown diamond-back.

Standing there rehearsing what I would do, I made

simple preparations. I tied three strings to the neck of each of two bags, cut a four-foot stick, and on this tied a narrow strap I had in my pocket to serve as a noose. That noose idea had been thought out in the sick room, and so had tying the strings on the bags. The necessary things were here, but somehow it all seemed new as I faced the tree.

With the bags over my arm and the stick in my right hand, I stalked toward the pine, my eyes boring into those out-thrust roots.

Nature, in her concealment, is a perfect artist. Within about twenty feet of the outside margin of the radial roots I saw nothing; but it was time to stop and stare intently. Then I made out two outlines. One was dark and looked like little more than a circular shadow; the other, also circular, was lichen-green. With my eyes now focusing, I made out two other shapes, much smaller and fitting into hollows as if to make them flush with the surface. All of them were diamond-backs and this was only one side of the tree. The nearest green-gray coil had a rattle protruding, shaped to a point, showing its owner to be young and still growing. My knowledge of diamond-backs was as yet slight, but I decided that the youngest was the star of the bevy. Tongues were flashing and heads turned my way, but I had approached so slowly that no harsh sound of a rattle disturbed the picture.

Backing up, I laid a bag on a bed of pine needles, tied one string upward to the branch of a seedling and pegged the lateral strings outward. The mouth of the bag gaped open in the shape of a triangle. My idea was to slip the noose under the flat head of the greenish snake and swing it to the clear brown bed near the bag. I accomplished this, but what a revelation in thrashing body and what a tumult of sound as the others went into action.

Now my prize was in a circular fighting coil near the bag, neck arched, eyes glittering as it watched me. The head had been snatched from the noose as I swung the creature to the ground and released the tension. No harm had been done beyond a ruffling of reptilian feelings, and by poking that tense coil, I backed it up, in its shuffling change of position, toward the mouth of the bag and within the canvas, when I made a rush, upended the bag—and the rattler slid to the bottom. I tied the bag. Turning to see the others I found them gone.

Stalking around my tree, for there were more big roots and declivities, I reached the area on the opposite side and greeted the sight of three big rattlers, closely grouped with an expression handed down from my father:

"Great day in the morning!"

The orgy ended in my bagging another, the rest making a dignified exit down a hole as deep and black as a woodchuck's burrow, their rattles fading to a faint, underground rustle, proving my conjecture that there was a subterranean chamber.

This was enough. I had found the tree. My dream

had been realized. I should have felt guilty if I had taken more. Moreover, the fascination of the spot was the thought that it would remain undisturbed.

The lugging of those heavy bags through the timber and back to the wagon was a fair-sized job; but, with my shirt soaked with sweat, I found the horse, who added to the festivities by giving a raucous whinny. Possibly the greeting was prompted by the thought of dry corn on the cob which I had in a bag for his meal. At any rate, he was soon munching and I was eating my greasy grit cakes. In the company of the bony nag, I thought of how this adventure had first come to my mind and of the advice of my nurse that I go north, where it was cool. I was in a completely satisfied, perspiring and conversational frame of mind, with nothing to talk to but a horse.

"Well, old man," I remarked, "we're a long way from Nova Scotia."

Despite a wide-flung panorama, there was less thrill in the quest of the coral king snake. The Florida pine had been like a framed picture that had come to life, and I had stepped right into it. In the realization of the California adventure, there were many things to see, drawing my interest this way and that.

The Californians ascend their mountains at what appears to be rash speed. Their idea is to go places quickly and the distance they cover in a day is astonishing. We skidded around turns of a road that was little more than a shelf against the mountain side. After varying grades we came to a region of tall pines—the hunting ground. The woodland giants had fallen, here and there. Soil about their roots had loosened from melting snows and some had been blown down. Others had been killed by lightning, rotted at the base and toppled over, leaving a marginal rim of jagged fragments.

Only one trunk in a dozen of the windfalls served my purpose. The resinous trunk of a pine long keeps the bark firmly attached. This was the condition of many. On others, the bark could be stripped, but it lay so close that nothing was to be found beneath but tracings of wood-boring larvae. The trunks warranting investigation were those on which slabs of bark had loosened and curled, making hiding places beneath. But then again, if such trunks lay in the blaze of the sun, the hollows beneath the slabs might be too hot for secretive reptile life. Hour after hour we searched for likely trunks, and during that day we found two of the coveted specimens. One was a yard long, broadly ringed with the brightest vermilion, the red separated by rings of cream-yellow, then margined by lustrous black. The larger specimen was found under a slab on a great pine that had carried away its root structure and lay at the angulation of an axle with a single, giant wheel attached. The incline was so sharp I had to sit on the trunk, pushing my way along as I lifted the loose bark. We had been hours at this work and the perch was precarious; my knocking away a small and unlikely slab and finding the first prize was almost an accident. The second snake was under a strip of bark that had fallen from a standing trunk, smooth and bare for the greater portion. This specimen was barely two feet long, but as with youthful snakes, more vividly colored than the adult. As it coiled in my hand, without attempt to escape, my friend remarked that it looked like a necklace of vari-colored coral, which, placed in a velvet-lined case, would seem to belong there, rather than in the bed of pulp where we had found it.

Our route lay over the divide to the desert slope. The second of my sick-room dreams was being checked off.

The desert offered new adventure, but I thought that the realization of this trip would rank second to the Florida reconnoiter in my memory. We hunted through canyons, caught lizards and chased whip snakes, which glide as fast as a man can run. After "miring" the car in sand and getting it out by breaking greasewood for traction, we looked like cooked lobsters. The thermometer on the tonneau rail registered 140.

"There's a government well about twenty miles ahead," said my companion. "We can soak our heads."

"I had a nurse," I told him, "who insisted that with my physique I should go where it's cool. She suggested Nova Scotia."

We used our last water bag to fill the radiator and went on.

Chapter VI

DEW IN THE DESERT

There had been an evening shower up the Chagres Valley in Panama, which had followed a few hours after the usual afternoon downpour. I had heard the steady advance of the rain through the jungle, an increasing roar like the approach of a train, until the deluge crashed on the corrugated roof of the engineers' shack. During the ten minutes of tumult I couldn't concentrate on my graphs of weather observations. Finally, it was over, and I went on with the pin-pricking process of recording variations in temperature and humidity.

That was the reason for my single light bulb burning after hours which brought a rumbling voice from the next room.

"For heaven's sake, put out that light. We'll be full of bugs."

The remark was followed by the appearance of the chief engineer, who stood in the doorway in much wrinkled pajamas.

As I swung around, a sheet of paper stuck to my forearm, pasted there with perspiration. The backs of my hands glistened with moisture.

"Hot and sticky," I remarked. "These graphs show day and night temperatures and percentage of humidity running nearly abreast. It's unusually warm to-night—let's see—88, and the mist following that shower is boosting the hygrometer close to the saturation point. Here's last night: temperature 72, humidity 70 per cent."

He closed the door behind him to keep his room in darkness.

"Do you know," he exclaimed, "some of these bugs get me dizzy. The screens keep out the big ones, but it's the confounded midges. There was one in my room flying a figure eight and another going around it in circles. The blooming things acted like an animated ad for automobiles."

He strode down the small hallway, where an electric refrigerator whirred the greater part of the time, and came back with ice, two glasses and liquid refreshments. He turned his back to the gyrations of a cloud of midges about my light, then served the drinks.

"Takes a bit of time to settle down to this—after surveying in Alaska—but I'm beginning to get interested in this place."

He told me that, after the preliminary blasting, the geologist with the party had pointed out three different types of marine strata, high up on the mountains, showing that three successive times, ages apart, the Isthmus of Panama had been the sea bottom, and then had been thrust into land formation; and that the last upthrust had been "recent," geologically speaking, for large and almost perfect shells could be chipped from the rocks. How long had it taken, he wondered, for the seeds of the great jungle forest to become spread, and animal life to emigrate across a new land-bridge extending northward from equatorial latitudes and southward from North America? For both phases of migration were indisputable. How long, he speculated, would it take snakes to extend their habitat? "At any rate," he concluded, "I've understood that reptiles like plenty of water and there is every inducement for them to spread over these parts."

With this, he said good night and went to his room. As I saw that there was an inch opening at the bottom of his door and that my room was populous with midges, I snapped off my light and went to bed.

That last remark of the engineer stuck in my mind. I'd give him a new slant in our talks. ". . . reptiles like plenty of water." He didn't realize that in pioneering many forms of reptile life had entered the deserts, had liked such domains, remained there, and undergone strange changes—in places where there were no rivers, brooks or springs, where rains were infrequent or almost unknown, and where, if they did occur, they immediately sank into the open waste leaving no trace. Only the year before, I had for the second time studied such species of reptiles in a place so different from this reeking moisture that it was like another world.

There was nothing much to do in the morning. But I

planned a late afternoon reconnoiter and a return over the trail at night. The picture of the desert, in the midst of this steamy background, though incongruous enough, seemed to stand out all the more clearly. That was as far as I got before I dropped asleep. But the idea cropped up again when I woke up.

The second desert reconnoiter came about as a result of two desires. One was to go volcano hunting, for volcanic eruptions had been one of my obsessions from boyhood and Mt. Lassen, in California, which had given a grand show in 1914 and 1915, showed signs of renewed activity. The other was to revisit the scenes of my brief desert adventures. In all of my wanderings I had to pass through certain spots rather hurriedly, of necessity. I remembered these spots and wanted to revisit and investigate them thoroughly. There had been canyons in the desert, oases with palm trees where investigation might yield fascinating results.

Gradually I was adding to my library volumes and special articles on volcanology. I had a fair-sized series of works at hand, but the knowledge of a real volcano going full blast in the United States in 1915 spurred my ambition to fill the shelves. Through the Geophysical Laboratory in Washington, I accumulated all the available data about Mt. Lassen. Possibly there are not many people in this country who realize what happened in California in 1914 and 1915—that a volcano in the Cascades went into action and shot tremendous clouds of pumice and eruptive vapors miles high; that red-hot volcanic bombs were hurled to the heavens, some of them weighing up to fifty tons; that seething clouds glowed red at night and lava descended. In May of 1915 came culminating blasts. Sections of forests with trees six to ten feet in diameter were knocked flat, like matchwood, and on the trunks of trees that remained standing the bark was blasted from one side so that it looked like cotton. Lava needles, hurled five miles high and following the upper westerly winds, fell as far as two hundred miles away. Fortunately the volcano stood in an uninhabited area, which is now a national park. There was no loss of life, but the blasts and the consequent desolation were equivalent to the destruction of Mt. Pelee on Martinique, not long before. All this happened in California when I couldn't be there. At the time I had a feeling of being cheated—of missing something in which I would have revelled. It was akin to my youthful disappointment at missing the fire at Quinn's Livery Stable.

Imagine, then, my delight, when a chance came to get away, to hear rumors that Mt. Lassen was opening again. I gave it time, for explosions from a resting crater are likely to develop gradually. Then I started west to Oregon with the idea of working south to Red Bluff, California, and going in toward Mt. Lassen from that point. I could be away only a month.

Since Fremont's westward exploring in 1840, when Mt. Baker in Washington was in heavy eruption, there have been no recurrences in that state. Mt. Hood, in

Oregon, however, has been kept under surveillance. It has an elevation of over eleven thousand feet, with a well-defined crater, on one side of which is a great fissure from which steam escapes steadily. At times the steam is dense enough to be seen for miles on a clear day. Under certain atmospheric conditions near the crater, the steam is particularly noticeable and, trailing off with cloud strata, has produced predictions that an eruption was beginning. Scientific observations near the summit, however, bring reports that there are no sulphurous fumes nor carbon monoxide, associated with volcanic eruptions. My view of Mt. Hood showed the majestic mass standing out in relief against a cloudless sky. The radial streaks of white from its snow slides gave the effect of utter calm. I gazed in vain for signs of steam or hints of volcanic activity.

The train ride into California offers a glorious panorama, with Mt. Shasta gradually looming ahead, disappearing in a swing of curves, then again dominating the background. It is a matter of hours from the time one first sees Shasta until one leaves it. Its snowy sides, as they stand serene, show in their profiles the history of thunderous times in the dim past. No more clearly defined craters could be imagined, but Shasta rests, from Pleistocene times, possibly never again to awaken.

The train neared Red Bluff, with a clear view of Mt. Lassen. A look at that peak would decide whether I stopped or went on. The conductor's information was not exciting. There had been little manifestation from

Lassen in some time. My binoculars showed the summit etched calm and clear against the sky; there was nothing to warrant an inquisitive stop. The mild perturbations were over. The alternative desert reconnoiter lay ahead.

Checking off volcanic possibilities, with a mixture of disappointment and anticipation that there might be something later on, I planned my route toward southern California. I had some ideas—again they were concerned with certain spots. We reached one definite point after a broiling trip by motor over a desert trail with only fair traction. Here was a canyon of ancient lava, where a spring rushed from crevices to form a stream one hundred yards long which again sought innumerable crevices by which to return whence it came, and was absorbed after its short progress into dry and shifting sands. Along its external, gushing route was a dual row of palms looking as ancient as if they had stepped out of a prehistoric landscape. Their "skirts" from dead and down-drooping leaves were six feet in diameter, but the green tops and the presence of water suggested an oasis to me. In the earlier desert trip we had stopped here momentarily, but had had to press on. I had remembered this oasis as a probable mecca for desert reptiles, if it were carefully searched; and here we were.

On the sides of the canyon were shelving ledges, favorable for rattlesnakes. It was late afternoon and cooling off, the cliffs shading the canyon—the ideal time to start hunting. I had not been clambering over the rocks five minutes before I heard the buzz of a rattler. I saw him escape into a crevice, and the buzz faded out. Search as we did, past sunset and into the early evening when some of the desert forms, chiefly the poisonous snakes, often emerge, that was the only sign of life that our prying, prowling and watching revealed in this anticipated hunting-ground. The attraction of that spring turned out to be nothing but theory. We found our specimens in the open wastes with no inclination to congregate near the pictured oases.

Working south toward the tree yucca belt, we ascended a ridge of ancient lava and stopped the car to view the far-flung desert stretches from an elevation. To the west rose the serrated wall of the Sierra Nevada, with its passes to the coastal region made clear by gashes in the lower slopes, as red as brick dust. Stretching eastward like the sea, to meet a distant horizon, was the desert, spotted in the near distance and further off appearing freckled with patches of greasewood and sage.

What a change had come over this vast domain since past ages—and what had caused it? In Pleistocene times, this far-flung region had been the grazing grounds of the most magnificent aggregation of animals the world has ever known—elephants, rhinoceroses, giant deer, many kinds of camels, from small creatures to towering brutes with necks longer than giraffes, herds of horses of all shapes and sizes from slender creatures smaller than a pony to majestic equines far heavier and higher than the big draft animals finally bred by man. The herds were preyed upon by giant wolves, lions and

South African zonure. Styles in spikes and bristles are worn all over the world among desert lizards.

North African mastigure. Unrelated to the upper figure and with a habitat widely separated, the mastigure displays the world-wide tendency for spiky decoration of desert types.

Cholla belt of the southwestern desert, with no trace of water for miles and autos as rare as ships at sea.

A desert whip snake that can outdistance a man at a run and receives liquid nourishment from surface dew.

saber-toothed tigers. The fossil bones of these legions are scattered all over the far West. What happened to change the grazing grounds to deserts might be theoretically attributed to the chain of the Sierra Nevada and Cascades going aflame in volcanic outburst, and attending cataclysmic storms wearing away top soils from surfaces which ages before had been invaded by the sea and its sand. That there had been great distress among the remnants of those mammal legions is evident from their piled-up fossils around ancient water holes in California. But the hot waste that was left was not to remain uninhabited. Reptile life crept to its edges, became adapted for further pioneering, and attained high specialization for a desert life.

In some instances specialization was carried to extremes. Lizards acquired fringed toes to enable them to run over fine sand without sinking; spiny scalation similar to desert plants served as protective or simulating covering; protective coloration was evolved, and many snakes developed speed so they could skim rapidly over the surface. The slower snakes acquired wedge-shaped snouts for burrowing into the sand; the development of the larger species was toward slender form and speed. A rattlesnake, finally taking its abode upon the wastes, passed through phases of adaptation, until in perfected form—to keep its proportionately heavy body from sinking into the sand—it threw out flat, lateral loops and relinquished the gliding gait of its kin. Of all places, it would seem that these hot wastes, devoid of water except in scattered canyons, would repel reptile life, yet in all warm parts of the world, the deserts are inhabited by many specialized kinds.

The most interesting specimens obtained on that trip were the horned "toads." There are a dozen kinds of these flat-bodied lizards with short tails. Some have a pair of long horns on the head and others have very short horns or mere tubercles. A kind in southern Arizona has a circlet of large flat horns, like a crown; while another, in the boundary region, has no sign of horns and is very toad-like. We found most remarkable specimens on blackish lava slopes. Mixed with the lava were yellow particles the size of one's finger nail. The first specimen surprised us by almost running from under my feet. I had seen the little lump on the dark, igneous rock, but I had thought it was a chip of lava. It was blackish with scattered yellow spots. And we found others of coloration precisely matching the surface on which they lived, in heat which would seem almost unendurable for small creatures. In an area of pinkish desert we found pink specimens with scattered markings like pebbles. They were extremely difficult to see unless they were moving. If pursued, their tendency was to run under clumps of sage. At such places, late in the day, we saw specimens "digging in" to sleep. The "toad" ducked its wedge-shaped snout into the sand and worked forward, shoving its head from side to side. In this way it plowed into the sand until its back was lightly covered. The horns and eyes remained above the surface, but it took the keenest kind of investigation to find a hiding specimen in a square yard of sand, if bits of prickly débris of desert plants were scattered on the surface.

I wondered how on earth these creatures could live in such places; how the aqueous content of their bodies was sustained or replenished. There hadn't been rain for months, and there was no water for miles.

A hint as to the answer came one morning at dawn. We had no camping equipment, having decided to dispense with this complication by sleeping in the car, one on the front seat and the other in the back. The seats of an automobile serve as only a fairly comfortable couch. One's knees must be doubled up, and with a dufflebag for a pillow, there are many twistings and turnings during the night. Moreover, the temperature of the desert takes a downward plunge during the night. I awakened shivering and pulled up the floor mat as covering. It was not conducive to much greater comfort. My companion, I noticed, had crawled down to the floor, removed and overturned the front seat cushion and, in a blink of the flash light, appeared to be buried under coiled springs.

"Uh-h," he grunted. "It's cold."

About three A.M. the car started to heave. We had awakened simultaneously.

"Cold!" was the unanimous exclamation.

We started the engine and raced it. It seemed as if the radiator were determined to match the general chill, but at last we felt a tepid warmth. We pressed our backs and stomachs against it and, thinking that heat had filtered from the underbody of the car, again crawled back under our coverings.

According to fiction, dawn steals out of the East in steely gray which gives way to roseate glow. What I remember about the coming day is that it was dawn, and it was cold. Throwing off the mat, I plunged through the sand for a straggling growth of sage. Fortunately for us this was dead around the edge; breaking away brittle fragments, and laying them over a page of a Los Angeles newspaper, I kindled a feeble fire. As I held my hands and wrists over the column of pungent smoke, the wan face of my companion peered over a forward door of the car.

"I'll start the coffee," he said sleepily.

The coffee was made, breakfast prepared and after intermittent yawns we were ourselves again.

The sun was rising, shooting long shadows from the car and the brittle clumps of what might have been called vegetation.

"You may laugh it off, Frank," I declared, "but when I broke away that stuff for the fire, it felt damp and it wasn't too easy to light it."

"What," he answered, "dew in the desert! That's a new one to me."

Nevertheless I retained that impression and later there was a strange solution concerned with the lives of the very types of creatures we were hunting.

With the rising sun the heat returned, and, following a government marked "road" which was not too apparent, owing to drifting sand, we worked toward the yucca belt. Several times we were worried when the tires sank deeply and the engine grunted with the strain, and particularly when no sage was in sight—for broken branches of this pallid bush are the remedy for tough spots in American desert traction.

We reached the yuccas—weird forests of bayonet plants, growing fifteen to twenty feet high, the stalks a mass of down-dropping dead leaves topped by little more than a bouquet of lanceolate, spiked vegetation. The growth springs from soil as dry as talcum powder. Once a year there are short rains. It would seem as if this respite from burning heat must be stored in those spectral trunks and last for interminable months.

On the sandy floor of the yucca forest are many dead trunks, fallen pellmell. There are also heaps of the elongated dead leaves or "bayonets." The purpose in coming to this region was to hunt for a small lizard, which is to be found nowhere else in the United States. It lives among the fallen débris, or hides under the dead leaves drooping from the stalks of the yuccas.

This family of lizards is curious. It is called by scientists the *Xantusiidae* and has been popularly referred to as the family of Night Lizards. It is a small grouping, comprising three genera and a total number of less than a dozen kinds. A single species inhabits Central America; another lives in Cuba; the balance inhabit the deserts of California and Lower California. Their existence in the New World is one of the brain-racking problems of zoölogists, since they appear to be allied to an extensive family which is exclusively Old World. These small scampering creatures, however, have been accorded distinct family recognition because they have no eyelids, the eyes being protected by a cap-like glassy covering. Moreover, the eyes have elliptic, or cat-like, pupils which, among lizards—except the little granular-skinned geckoes—is abnormal.

We obtained a series of specimens by searching among the débris. They were light brown, speckled with darker marks, and barely four inches long, though they appeared to be full-grown. My speculation was that such delicate creatures in captivity could be fed only on "banana flies," which are an old stand-by to the herpetologist in feeding very small lizards, and seem to drop out of the sky, or spontaneously increase in numbers, if stale fruit is allowed to sicken.

The night was not so cold in the yucca belt, although we were still not comfortable. We played a flash light among the stalks after dark, and, while we heard occasional scamperings and several times saw small figures in motion, a slap of the hand landed on nothing. We would have done better to hunt them during their diurnal sleep.

At dawn I again collected débris to start a fire. Never again, I vowed, as my eyes burned from the pungent smoke and my fingers and wrists sought the ascending heat, would I come into the desert without a blanket—a horse blanket. Once again there was that feeling of dampness among the scrapings used to start the fire.

"I wish I had a hygrometer to bury in this stuff," I complained. "I'll bet we'd get a moisture reading."

"That's the last piece of junk I'd think of bringing in here," grunted Frank. His back was squeezed against the radiator as the motor shook the car. "We've only two water bags left for this bus and, unless we strike a government well to-day, we're out of luck."

It was toward noon that we struck a "well," a circular trough with an artesian pipe in the center from which we replenished the water bags, and then hung them around the car. The range loomed close to the westward and we headed for a pass that would take us into the habitable parts of California.

An incident connected with one of our serpent captives stands out. As we headed for the grades—but were still in the sand—a whip-like snake, about four feet long, glided to the shelter of what looked like little more than the corpse of a bush of radial sticks. The brakes squealed. I made a run for the bush and recognized the snake. It was a striped desert racer, the posterior part of its body tinged with coral pink, one of the most slender and speedy of the desert types. It turned as I approached, its tongue flashing at such tension that its head quivered. As I made a rush to grasp it, it doubled in rectangular fashion from its forward rush, and shot under the car. Frank jumped out and went after it, but it turned again. We were hampered by the sand, but anyone could have seen we were trying to run. That snake kept ahead of us and would not have been captured had it not retreated among a mass of gnarled roots from which the sand had drifted. There has been speculation about the speed of which snakes are capable; that reptile outdistanced our efforts to catch it in the open.

As we ascended into the pass, we stopped to pick up a desert king snake, with milk-white rings, and farther up, we ransacked a canyon where there were pools of blood-warm water connected by a sickly brook. Here we caught a dozen western garter snakes, which slid into the water as we approached but were easily traced. They lived the lives of water snakes, in fact they were water snakes—as are most of the members of the garter snake genus to be found west of the Mississippi. A few hours later we descended among the orange groves.

Tabulating the desert catch and packing the specimens into flat boxes for shipment East, I listed the following:

Twenty-two horned "toads," representing two species; three desert iguanas; two chuckawallas; six zebra-tailed lizards; four fringe-toed lizards; one pink-bellied racer; four striped racers; one ringed king snake; twelve western garter snakes and two horned rattlesnakes or sidewinders.

It was an interesting series to show from a fascinating trip.

This collection hints at the variety of reptile life that has invaded the desert, but the picture is vague when compared to the scientific listing of reptiles that are known to live in that hot and dry southwestern portion of the United States. There are fourteen genera of lizards, with over sixty species, and eleven genera of snakes with close to thirty kinds. Only a few of the lizards are nocturnal. Among the snakes there is a higher percentage of night-prowling kinds, and with the diurnal species, a tendency to seek what midday "shade" can be found by moving from bush to bush. It has been found, in fact, that the snakes are unable to endure continued exposure to the sun. The lizards have much greater endurance to its direct rays.

When the collection arrived in New York, the problem was to discover how such creatures could be maintained under artificial conditions. Sand was decided on as a proper stratum for the cages and two methods of maintenance were tried. While the room temperature was seventy-five degrees or over, it was decided, with part of the series, to heat the sand moderately by low wattage lamps burning beneath the cages. The greater number of the specimens shuffled into the sandy medium at night, their sides imbedded, backs protruding. When we used moderately heated sand, there was fairly successful longevity. In "cold" sand there was erratic feeding and gradual loss of specimens. Exposure to sunshine, even though the room temperature was high, was found to be necessary. Some of the lizards would take their insect food only in the sunlight. Flying kinds of insects were of no use, since desert lizards are not adept at climbing and stalking them. The horned "toads" were more difficult to feed because they were slower in going after their prey. Crawling insects were essential and we tried ants with fair success, but the "toads" would not take the kinds which carried a body taste of formic acid, common among ants. Not having studied ants to the extent of being able to distinguish the odoriferous kinds from those that were palatable to horned "toads," I rolled specimens between my fingers and learned that some ants smell like perfume while others have no odor. Certain little black ants were particularly liked and the horned "toads" lapped them up at a rate of approximately thirty to forty a minute, by protruding a sticky little knob which represented the tongue.

The main difficulty with the lizards was to induce them to take water. Few would drink from pans imbedded in the sand. We had fair results in coaxing them to lap hanging drops from fine branches dipped in a pail. I realized that all were desert types and not accustomed to see water, but there was slow enervation among them, despite what appeared to be an abundance of food. With the exception of half a dozen horned "toads," the last of the lizards died about a year later. The snakes lived much longer, since they were less difficult to feed and would drink from shallow pans. From my problems in caring for that collection, I realized how unfortunate were the many horned "toads" brought to the North by tourists as souvenirs. They live only as long as a reptile can slowly starve to death—a matter of a few weeks.

The puzzling point of maintaining the aqueous content of an animate body remained in my mind, for even creatures of the deserts must receive water in some way. Even though there are no brooks or springs, there must be some way, somehow, possibly by absorption— There was an idea! Frogs and toads never drank, but absorbed water through their skin. Some lived in quite dry places and depended upon absorption of dew through their tender skins. Lizards were clad with scales, but many of them showed patches of granular skin between the scales. I remembered that feeling of dampness when I was gathering débris among the sage. At the time, we had decided that it was the gathering chill which made the branches feel cold, but here was a possibility—dew in the desert! There was a scientist of high standing who could verify such a possibility—Dr. D. F. MacDougal, of the Laboratory for Plant Physiology, a division of the Carnegie Institution of Washington. I wrote him and received the following reply:

"Dew may be formed almost anywhere in deserts. I have waked up in various parts of North America to find my sleeping bag and everything around us glistening with it; one of the heaviest deposits I have ever experienced was in the Libyan desert, in a place in which no rain had fallen for years. I believe it also occurs in the dry strip of western South America, although I cannot cite you to the accounts of it. It is mentioned only casually by most writers and it would be difficult to find references. I have something better—my own experiences."

Because of this information and the subsequent spraying of the basal patches of vegetation in desert cages, where reptiles hide to sleep or lightly burrow, the necessary absorption through their skins will probably solve the problem of their successful maintenance.

And so my thoughts reverted to the remarks of the engineer in Panama. He made no pretense of being a naturalist and his ideas about reptiles living chiefly in damp places did not give the correct picture of their modern distribution. Nevertheless, his theory carried a strong element of truth. The reptile clan sprang into being many millions of years ago on an earth whose combinations of heat and humidity are unequalled to-day. Over world-wide swampy areas the prehistoric reptiles increased in size and numbers. The background was soggy soil and water. With the decrease in size and numbers to the remnants living to-day, there remains the reptilian instinct for water. This would point to slow pioneering to new methods of life over the plains and into the deserts. Such gradual marches, which produce distribution, are usually actuated by the sense of leaving common enemies behind. But, in accordance with the theory advanced here, the movement into the sterile areas, the slow relinquishment of regions of springs and brooks, was through the dew stratum. They pushed on to what appear, to the panting human, appalling wastes, but still the life-sustaining moisture was to be found and provided a means of existence for forms becoming strangely changed from their relatives of the damp, equatorial belts.

Chapter VII

NEW SLANTS AT THE MONKEYS

During my care of the collection of warm-blooded animals at the New York Zoölogical Park, I have had experiences with elephants, hoofed stock, lions, tigers, bears, kangaroos and monkeys. The person in charge of such a variety of beasts has grave responsibilities. Most of his charges, however, have unflagging appetites; they give no trouble in that direction. While I have long objected to the importation by animal dealers of delicate species that are unhappy in captivity, such languishing animals come along now and then, miserable waifs soon to die unless they are given the wisest care. But if they do get such attention, the study of their needs and why they are spiritless offers fascinating problems for the sympathetic student of animals.

Problems of special care are not infrequent among New World monkeys, most of which are less hardy than Old World kinds. Among them are species which, with ordinary attention, survive only a few months. I have tried to stop the general shipping of such kinds as the titi, saki, uakari and howling monkeys, among South American mammals. However, one of these howling monkeys arrived at the Park in a batch of very decrepit small creatures brought north by an explorer.

"You will never be able to keep that monkey alive in the Park," said my daughter, when she saw the young red howling monkey from Honduras.

This was not flattering, in view of the fact that we have a fine monkey house of fancy brick with terra-cotta trimmings, elaborate cage arrangements, and a staff of trained keepers.

The young howler glowered from its travelling cage, its back arched and its shoulders slumping. I realized what my daughter had meant. Here was a species of leaf-eating monkey, of particularly morose disposition—as are many Central and South American monkeys. They lack the vivacity and playful spirit of other types. There is a genus of leaf-eating monkeys in Africa having specially constructed stomachs with several compartments, like a cow, but they are not so mopy as the New World howlers; they take kindly to captivity and readily to a nourishing diet. Other kinds are extremely temperamental, and a scare, even in transferring them from one cage to another, may shock them into illness. Then, of course, there are many of the hard-boiled kinds, the rhesus, macaque, green and vervet monkeys that are cage rowdies, screeching, indulging in acrobatics, fighting—who thrive for years.

My daughter took the red howler to our home, where

we have netted enclosures for observation specimens. The attitude of the animal was not savage but sullen and resentful of the change that had come into its life. It was not one of the leaping, destructive kind that must be kept in a cage the greater part of the time. When she took it into the house and coaxed it from the travelling cage, it settled on the arm of a chair, its shoulders drooping, with a moody expression as if it were awaiting what was going to happen next.

The howler was thin and had probably eaten just about enough to keep it alive on its voyage from the tropics. Its first nourishment was a stock solution we have found efficient with delicate monkeys. (We mix about a pint at a time and keep it in the icebox.) My daughter put two tablespoonsful of a solution of cod-liver oil emulsion into a pint of tepid water and added a tablespoonful of sweetened condensed milk. This is the only fluid given to a monkey of this kind. Its water content is ample to satisfy thirst and the codliver oil is a preventive against rickets. The condensed milk is added simply because the monkeys like it.

We offered the sulking howler the mixture on a teaspoon, but he turned up his nose. We assumed a gentle but stern attitude and presented the spoon from various angles, until the animal, in the face of this insistence, condescended to put his lips to the spoon. One taste was enough. There was a glimmer of interest in his dull eyes and he supped the spoon dry. After that he consumed a dozen spoonfuls.

"He'll be all right," said my daughter, as she lifted the slouching figure from the chair and walked off with it.

That was the beginning of a friendship, and soon she and the homely waif were inseparable. We never considered him a cage animal. Each night we brought him into the house and he slept in a dog basket on a padded cushion, sometimes wandering to my daughter's bed and cautiously cuddling at the edge of the pillow, where he woke her with his snores. He accompanied us on two long journeys, because we would entrust him to nobody's care. He died after two years, from what appeared to be influenza, when that malady swept through the family. But his span of life had broken all known records for the maintenance of a captive howling monkey.

The story of our rearing of that delicate animal is typical of what may be done by close individual attention. From the records of the Zoölogical Society of London, covering a period of close to seventy-five years, the average life of captive howling monkeys reaching Europe appears to be three and a half months. Among all the specimens exhibited, the longest record is thirteen months. Of specimens which arrived at the Zoölogical Park in New York and were placed in the cages with the other monkeys, none lived longer than three months.

Howling monkeys attain a considerable size, weighing over twenty-five pounds when adult and then having a length, including body and tail, of close to five feet. The adult is grotesque, with heavy head and coal-black face. The thick beard is black, while the body is clad with reddish hair. The adult males have powerful canine teeth over an inch long. The most remarkable thing about them is their deep, throaty cry, rendered possible by the enlarged development of the hyoid process or "Adam's apple," which forms a sound box, swelling to large proportions as the animal howls or, more correctly, roars. I have heard the troops in the jungle tree tops, and they sounded like lions. All of this was very interesting to my daughter. Since her charge was less than two feet long, we decided that it was not more than a few months old.

For the first few months the diet consisted of cereals cooked very thin, and small quantities of milk. The meals were provided three times a day. The infant took his food grudgingly; in fact, it had to be forced on him with a spoon, and at times, he would close his mouth tightly and turn his head away like a stubborn child. But the feeding operations seemed to convince him that we were thinking of his welfare. Soon he insisted on being coddled like a small child when any member of the family sat down.

Beef stew, containing a lot of vegetables, being an ideal diet for hardy monkeys, we tried it on the howler, in spite of his supposed vegetarian habits. "Red" was interested; he caught a bit of meat from the spoon and showed joy. Then he reached into the bowl for more. Though I had noticed the fondness of many monkeys for meat, this was a surprise, because the howler was less

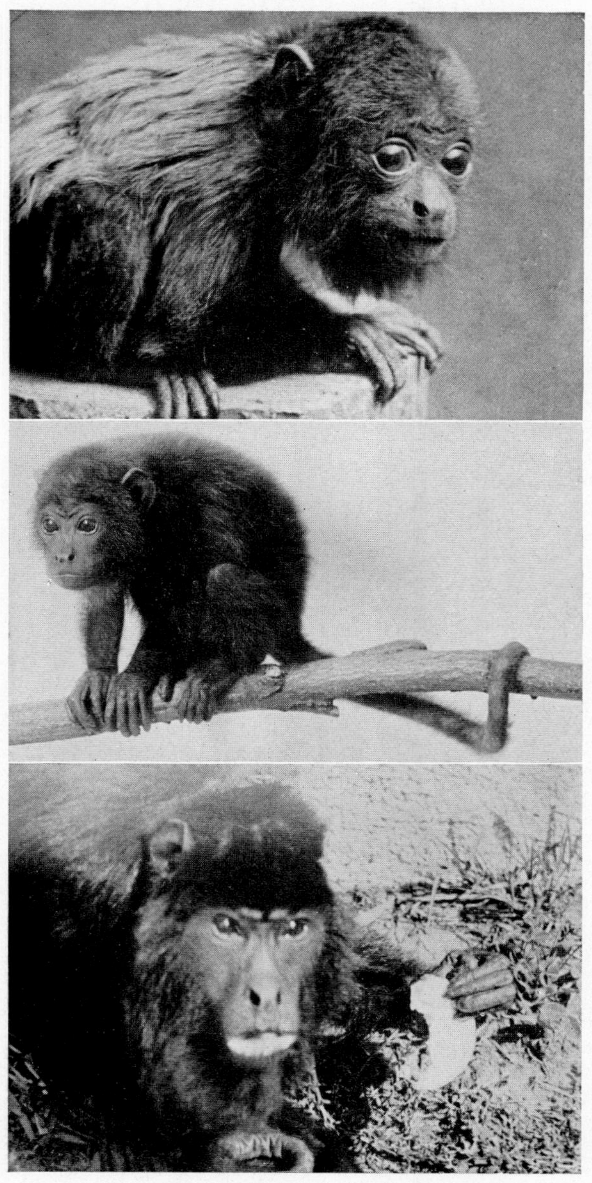

From infancy to adulthood with the South American howler monkey. Allegedly very delicate as a captive, the species was successfully reared after a study of its curious psychology.

During baby days some kinds of strong and hardy monkeys are highly amusing; but with development come manifestations showing that the greater number make dubious pets.

The average outcome with a "pet" monkey.

than a third grown. Chicken and several kinds of fruit were added to his diet. He regarded bananas, a standard monkey diet, with indifference, and accepted boiled vegetables. Quite by accident we found "Red" to be keen on spaghetti. We discovered this when he climbed upon the arm of my daughter's chair during lunch. Ordinarily he was quite sedate while we were dining, but on this occasion the spaghetti appeared worth a trial. He dived in, secured two writhing handfuls, and devoured it strand by strand.

Apparently the reputation that such monkeys have as "delicate" captives comes from an unhappy mental state when their appetite languishes. "Red" was a member of the family; he had been taught cleanly habits and had the run of the house. Under these conditions his digestive system was anything but delicate. This was afterward doubly checked when my daughter went for a swim at the beach, leaving him with some children. They entertained him by feeding him a frankfurter, roll and sauerkraut, then gave him a drink of sarsaparilla. Arriving home after this orgy, he committed one of his rare indiscretions by eating the frosting from a meringue pie.

As the monkey developed, his howlings and roaring, always uttered in what appeared to be a cheerful spirit, became a source of embarrassment since the people outside hinted that we harbored lions or tigers.

He was afraid of and mystified by a human sneeze, since his vocabulary contained no such sound. If anyone sneezed, he would glance at the nearest window, then rush for shelter. He usually hid under a heavy chair, to emerge slowly and glance cautiously toward all the windows in the room. He showed no fear of the person who sneezed but seemed to consider the sneeze a warning to take cover.

When he approached the end of the second year as a captive, his outlines clearly indicated the sinister form of the adult howler—the canines were now very evident, and a bony brow protruded over his glittering dark eyes. Natural history books have declared the adult howler to be savage and morose, but not so with "Red." He looked but did not act the part. I never knew him to break anything in the house. He solemnly inspected many things, but made no attempt to pick up anything unless it was small. Moreover, he never knocked over a vase or glass. This was remarkable in comparison with most species of monkeys, which if liberated will wreck the contents of a room.

This does not prove that the howler lacked all vivacity. He liked to be played with as one plays with a dog—to be rolled on his back and wrestled, while he uttered explosive grunts, his generous mouth widespread in an unmistakable grin. He lorded it over the cat and dog, the former a particularly large, lazy animal. If we made a motion to shoo the cat out of the way, he would rush at her and end the performance with a slap and a grunt. They were good friends, but "Red" was the disciplinarian. And so the study of "Red" offered something new in monkey psychology.

Another study of an allegedly delicate monkey—but a particularly attractive one—was that of the golden or the lion marmoset. The zoos have long sought this singularly beautiful monkey, but records of its longevity as a captive, both in Europe and America, tell a sad story—an average life of but a few months.

I had seen this type of marmoset in the tropics, a sort of miniature monkey. Its pelage is like the head of a platinum blonde. From its shoulders tumbles a mass of lustrous, pale golden hair, like the mane of a lion—from which comes its name. From my observation of these miniatures on the horizontal branches of the big ceiba trees, I had decided that they were insect and lizard hunters—not fruit eaters, except as a diversion. Discovering a pair in New York and seeing the dealer's anxiety to get rid of them, I bought them at a fair price for the species, which is usually as much as fifty dollars a pair, because of their beauty. I was warned by my associates that they would live but a few months, but I kept mum, for I had other ideas. The European record for longevity appeared to have been nine months. By careful feeding I have established a record of five years with the original specimens who are still living. Their diet is largely composed of insects and small lizards. Fortunately the latter are always available, since I keep a supply on hand for the rear-fanged snakes, some of which will take nothing else. The pair of golden marmosets yielded interesting scientific data. They bred twice, the progeny in each case being twins, and the young attained full growth in the surprisingly short time of ten months, showing a vast difference from the slow development of the larger monkeys who reach maturity in from three to five years, and the apes who take nine to ten years.

The more I see of the ordinary kinds of monkeys and their inconsistencies, the more I realize that their psychology is hard to work out. This was illustrated by the recent case of the "pet" of a veteran vaudeville trouper, a lady of emphatic manners and voice, who seemed sophisticated in all things except the ways of monkeys. She came to my office carrying a macaque monkey in a basket, and the way that basket jumped up and down on the floor gave evidence that the imp inside had plenty of vigor. As she removed the animal on a chain, it pulled back its forehead and made an insolent "face" at me, until its eyebrows were nearly on the top of its head. I asked her to keep a grip on the chain, for I had a mental picture of ink wells and stationery flying in all directions.

Her story was sad. She had had a pet monkey of that kind for several years, but it had died of colic. It had been very affectionate, sleeping on her pillow every night. The only trouble with it, she said, was its antagonism to her friends, its inclination to leap upon anyone, without warning, and bite. That difficulty was easily averted, however, by locking the monkey in a room by itself when guests were expected. When it died, she told me, she had cried for a week, untii a gentleman friend, moved to pity, had bought a second monkey for her.

Now, incongruous as it may seem, the new monkey

wanted to make pals of her friends but was antagonistic to her, although she provided it affectionately with every item known in a monkey's diet. It readily enough slept on her pillow, but every time she turned, it bit her. She exhibited a profusion of black and blue marks of varying intensity, and said that, since she had heard that monkey bites might be poisonous, she kept caustic pencils on her bureau.

I told her that, despite an old supposition, the bite of a monkey was no more dangerous than that of any other animal of similar size. Then I suggested that she get rid of the mean little beast. This latter remark was unfortunate. The lady declared that she had no intention of seeking such a solution. What she wanted to know was how hard she should slap the monkey to correct its ways. I am afraid my advice did not satisfy her, for I told her that a slapped monkey of that ruffian type usually screeches its head off and comes right back for another round. The lady left with a promise that she would report results, but I have heard nothing further from her.

I had taken one of my keepers to the surgeon's to have a rip in his shoulder from a gibbon's bite cleaned and fixed up. I was back at the monkey house talking to the Senior Keeper Palmer, and telling him that his assistant would be back in a few days.

"He should have looked him in the eye, just as one shouldn't look a baboon or rhese monkey in the eye."

"What in the devil do you mean, Palmer? Look one in the eye and turn your head on the other!"

Palmer was insistent.

"A gibbon won't attack you if you look him in the eye. But a baboon, a rhese or macaque gets mad if you look at him. A gelada gets so mad he tears out his hair and goes nutty if you stare at him."

"So you stare all around and don't look directly at them—except the gibbons?"

"That's what I'll tell Reilly when he gets back," insisted Palmer.

"Be sure to tell him what he can look at, so he won't get the wires crossed," was my suggestion.

When you step up to the head of the class, you consider the anthropoid apes—the gorilla, chimpanzee and orang which are far superior to mere monkeys. We have examples that have been on exhibition over twenty years' time. Some weigh not much over a hundred pounds, but could murder a human—and would, with glee. They impress me as raging examples of primatology more attractively represented by younger specimens, which are intensely interesting as a study in animal psychology.

An alleged proof of the twisted mentality of the adult anthropoid which sticks in my mind is brought out in an article in *Time*, of February 2, 1936. It relates to sanctuaries for African animals and reads in part:

"The gorilla was given absolute protection because it is naturally amiable, while the chimpanzee, which has acquired the habit of kidnapping native children and dropping them from trees, was relegated to the partially protected list."

Yale University maintains a department in Florida where the mental capacities of these apes are being intensively studied by a staff of scientists. Not long ago I heard of some unrelated but similar studies in the North, which had a curious ending.

A prominent doctor and his wife were asked to add a young chimpanzee to their household where there was a young child. The idea was to notice the influence of the child upon the ape, the latter to undergo a sort of kindergarten course, with the supposition that the ape would become refined and affect the mannerisms of the child. The child and ape were inseparable.

After several months, however, the parents noticed with anxiety that the child was developing ape expressions, protruding lip motions and a vocabulary aside from English that sounded more appropriate to the tree tops than the nursery. The culmination of embarrassment came during a visit of the grandparents, when the child displayed a new tendency—to scratch, with her fingers distended. This ended in the chimpanzee being sent back to the animal psychologists.

Reverting to the smaller monkeys, and hence down the scale, I am reminded of a recent scientific paper which demonstrated that they are likely to be affected by various tropical ailments. They suffer from malaria, enlargement of the liver, and intestinal parasites. This may account for the grouchy disposition of some individuals, since any trouble with the liver has a deleterious effect upon the temper.

In a recent issue of *The Journal of Mammalogy* there was a formal scientific article, the title of which might seem startling to the layman, but immediately attracts the interest of students of animal psychology. It was *Sham Louse-Picking, or Grooming, Among Monkeys.* Here is an explanation of upper shelf activities, commonly noticed to the amusement of the visiting public. I had often figured out that the manifestations were like the serving of afternoon tea—a courtesy in greeting guests, a polite gesture, in fact. To my embarrassment, at times, some of our tame monkeys had extended the gesture to fur coats and muffs, and even the heads of distinguished visitors. My explanation had been that it was a gesture of friendliness. It didn't always go over as a satisfactory explanation of the incident.

This scientific article demonstrates that monkeys do not systematically search for "fleas," since, as a rule, they are clear of external parasites. They search for minute salty crystals deposited on the skin, even plucking away hairs to obtain the exudate. So, after reading this article, I am able to explain to a visitor that the manifestation is for "exudates," but I have noticed that this polite scientific phraseology does not always ease the tension brought about by a cordial monkey's activities.

In the past I have advised against monkeys as pets, on the grounds that the greater number of species are too nervous, erratic, or really devilish to be turned loose. This criticism has been picked up and thrown back at

Durukuli, or owl monkey. South America has a number of small types which are difficult to maintain as captives. This species is nocturnal and feeds largely on insects.

Uakari monkey. Another delicate kind of the South American tropics. Unless receiving the keenest and most sympathetic care, its life as a captive is but a few months.

South American woolly monkey. One of the few species remaining gentle and trustworthy from infancy to maturity. It lives at elevations up to 8,000 feet and can endure considerable cold.

An African baboon and a Celebes "ape" embarrass a visitor by sham flea picking, a habit which the text describes in detail.

me in the form of many exceptions. I have been informed that I have forgotten the woolly monkey, douracouli, saki, squirrel and titi monkeys, all of South America. I had not forgotten them, but from motives of mercy I had eliminated reference to the smaller kinds, since they are extremely delicate, and require a partial insect diet and plenty of sun. True enough, the greater number of specimens of all the species are gentle and confiding, but, in the hands of anyone who has not carefully studied their requirements, they succumb to digestive troubles or develop rickets and soon die. The woolly monkey, standing at the head of the list, is an exception, but I have not recommended it as a pet because of the possibility of dealers bringing in too many of them to fall into kindly but incompetent hands.

Among all monkeys I have studied, the woolly stands by itself as a mixture of calm temperament and attractiveness. It is a large monkey, heavily coated with pelage like wool of the finest fiber. The usual color is lustrous silvery gray. I have never seen a savage specimen, even among the old males with long canine teeth. In examining occasional arrivals among the animal dealers, I have had no hesitation in opening a cage, and the woolly would climb into my arms in an immediate attempt to gain a friend. The opening of a cage with most kinds of monkeys—exceptional individuals excluded—means a screech and scurry to get away and a savage bite if restrained.

Answering my objecting correspondents, most of

whom have cited the strangely docile woolly monkey and claimed that it was a "hardy" species in captivity, I should like to say that we have one of these monkeys at home. True enough, it has long been in good health, but it is given two carefully selected meals each day, containing a variety of uncooked green vegetables, and, besides these, a preparation of milk and beaten egg. The only time it is in a cage is at night. It lives in a south room and basks for hours in the sun—a necessity for all monkeys. Under this schedule it remains well and happy. All this sounds simple enough, but actually this monkey receives rather extraordinary care. I consider the woolly far less hardy than the rowdy types of monkeys that make rough and dangerous pets. For these reasons I do not recommend monkeys as pets.

A highly attractive but exceedingly temperamental captive is a monkey recently received at the Park. This species is the most remarkable of New World monkeys. It was brought to New York by Dr. Wolfgang von Hagen, a most successful emissary of conservation in conferring with the Ecuadorian government relative to converting the Galápagos Islands into a protected sanctuary for the strange forms of life existing in that miniature archipelago.

During the doctor's stay in Ecuador he acquired, from the eastern jungle area, a specimen of the pygmy marmoset, *Callithrix pygmaeus*, the smallest species of monkey in the world. Its range has been recorded as western Brazil but the Ecuador record extends it. Providing it chiefly with an insect diet, Dr. von Hagen kept it for nearly a year, then brought it to New York. Its total length, including the relatively long tail, is approximately twelve inches, and upon placing it upon the scales I found it to be slightly over four ounces in weight. It is full grown, as is attested by its proportionately long canine teeth. I have found it to be ravenously fond of small lizards, which form a considerable part of the diet of the larger marmosets—and by the larger kinds I mean those of the genus with a body as large as that of a squirrel. Looking at this tiny thing, which cuddles in the palm of one's hand, it seems a long step from the five hundred pound gorilla which branched from the main stem from which the primates had their origin.

CHAPTER VIII

PROBLEMS OF A BEAR HUNT

IT ALL started on a Monday morning that began like any other Monday morning. My car was run out of the garage and I had gone in for my laundry bag when the telephone rang.

The call was from the chief constructor of the Zoölogical Park. He said that a bear had escaped and that he was holding his arriving workmen at the gates, fearing they might be attacked as they went to their jobs. I asked him what kind of a bear it was, and he said it was a Himalayan bear. That type is not savage unless it is restrained, and I told the constructor to let his men go to their work. In half an hour I was at the northern boundary of the Park. Judging that the director had reached the Park ahead of me, since he lived closer, and without doubt had organized a searching force, I cruised along the outside wooded boundary, asking here and there if anybody had seen a bear. The answers to my questions indicated that the animal had remained within the area enclosed by a high mesh fence—about three hundred acres, much of it thickly wooded with rhododendrons and laurel. A guard opened the gate, all gates having been locked, and I continued to the bear dens, which is a fair hike from the entrance.

Once outside, I found out just which bear had escaped. In the long series of rocky dens a pair of Himalayan black bears had been on exhibition. The male weighed about two hundred pounds. The female was lighter. They were beautiful animals, lustrous black, with a white crescent covering the breast and extending onto the throat. In order to scrub the bear dens, the keepers had entered the enclosure every day. Neither animal had shown a disposition to attack; they weren't friendly, but neither were they inimical to the men. It was the larger, the male, which had in some way climbed past the incurving overhand, raided four beehives of the senior keeper, climbed and broken the branches of a wild cherry tree, dug a big hole in a flower bed, and, to all appearances, departed into the woods.

The director had already sent out two corps of men, about thirty all told, to search timbered parts of the Park, barns and cellars. More men were needed since the searchers were scattered, leaving islands of unexplored ground. The Park gates remained closed past opening hours for the first time in the nearly forty years of its history. The plan was to notice the temper of the animal, if the men found him. If he looked docile, they were to attempt to capture him with a big ring net. It is next to impossible to rope a bear, because of his stout neck and relatively small head, and his dexterity in turning his forefeet outward and clipping a noose off with his strong claws. If this didn't work and the animal started to run, he was to be shot. We made this decision because two sides of the Park faced congested residential districts.

Bears are the smartest of all carnivorous animals, relatively the most powerful, and the most treacherous. There is no animal more dangerous to the misinformed and too inquisitive human than a "tame" bear.

Bill Bridges, of the publication department, and I joined the hunt. We traversed half a mile of dense woods and came back through slopes of rhododendrons that looked like a jungle. Bill thought that the searchers would soon come on the bear. The morning was young. The animal would soon be tangled in the net, or if it was absolutely necessary, an end would be made of him.

"I hope it's over before there's much of a story comes out of it," said Bill. Being an ex-newspaper man he realized that a Park bear hunt had strong news value, but was not publicity of which we could be proud.

As we crossed a path we saw a blue-shirted figure at a police telephone. Little did either of us realize that this contact with the outside was going to build that bear hunt into a dramatic spectacle and cause excitement hitherto unknown in that or any other zoo.

The real beginning came ten minutes later. Bill and I had taken another angle and were crossing the service

The world's smallest species of monkey, the pygmy marmoset of western Brazil. The example is full-grown. Being heavily haired, it appears larger than it really is. It weighs 4½ ounces or about twice as much as a mouse.

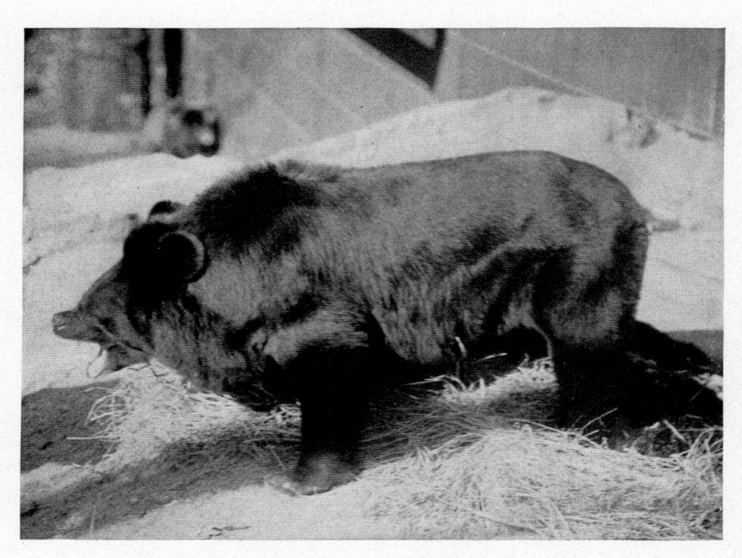

Himalayan bear in passive and dangerous moods. The escape of an animal of this kind was attended with criticism because the bear was shot. The erratic psychology of bears has brought distressing misfortunes among too trustful persons.

road when a police car rolled up with the captain and his driver. I had met the captain several times, and knew him to be a very efficient police officer.

"Doctor," said the captain, "could you use some of our men to help in the hunt?"

I explained the situation. There were two hundred acres of thick timber, with many hiding places. A line of beaters, spaced at equal distances, going through the woods would cover them completely and leave no unexplored spots. The captain went to the telephone.

When he returned I was shocked by his news of mobilization. Eight radio cars were on the way, two riot trucks and two prison vans—the latter commodious vehicles loaded with policemen!

Not many minutes had gone by when a wail of sirens converged on the Park. Shortly after, there was a clanging of bells and two handsome green trucks, rivalling the dash and glitter of the fire department, unloaded blue-shirted enthusiasts. The dingy prison vans rolled in immediately after, and discharged additional contingents. From the Buffalo Gate to a span of a quarter of the woodland area, the police lined-up like skirmishers. From the arsenals which those radio and riot cars discharged, I decided that such mobilization, equipment and discipline boded ill for the gangster racket and unlawful disturbances anywhere in the city.

Under orders from the captain, the line swung into the woods.

"Keep contact and alignment," he said. "Swing the wing at the north boundary and come back, sweeping new land to your left."

Very shortly a deputy commissioner took over the force of a hundred policemen. If the bear was seen, a shot was to be fired in the air.

As the time went forward, I again met Bill Bridges.

"Well, Bill, did we imagine there wouldn't be much of a story?"

Bill grinned. "Every paper in New York has somebody here and there's a battery of cameras."

We established two field headquarters—one in the north and another far to the south. The director was at the northern split of the staff. I joined the right flank of a turning wing. In nearly a mile of travel there was still no bear. The wing swung and went back. I dropped to the rear to pick up a carload of plain-clothes detectives who had joined the mobilization. In a swaying car, I followed the line through the woods.

There was a shot! We piled out of the car, which threatened to founder, and dashed ahead.

In front of the advancing line, which was tussling through leaves and crackling twigs, the bear had broken cover. The line halted and several keepers came up with a big net and ropes. The quarry showed every inclination to bolt—and keep going. It was vacation time and children were playing in the streets, near a group of apartment houses within sight. All this took place at the margin of "northern headquarters." The director gave orders to shoot the bear, and the animal was mercifully killed.

Following the newspaper stories of the hunt came an avalanche of protesting letters. We were criticized for our cruelty in shooting the bear, for the overwhelming odds of a police force and staff of keepers against a single animal. We were depressed at having to kill the bear, and chagrined that there could not have been a better ending to the story, but such are the vicissitudes of a zoo, with a critically watching public.

Not all escapes in a zoo—and they are rare—are attended by tragedy. The escape of an elephant recently demonstrated some interesting points of animal psychology, and had considerable humor.

This swift moving drama had as its central figure Alice, a wise and old, but still vivacious, Indian elephant. She had indulged occasionally in tantrums, but had never hinted at any intent to injure anybody. Twenty years before, she had bolted from her keeper while strolling for exercise through the Park, and had climbed through the massive doors of the reptile house, sweeping the frames with her as she plunged into the building. Years went by without further demonstration of temper, and she was used as a riding elephant. After several summers of traipsing around her big enclosure, taking visitors from a platform in a padded howdah on her back, she committed another indiscretion. Tiring of the promenading, she sidestepped to a post, carefully adjusted it against the forward frame of the howdah and shoved slowly. Elephant strength was too much for the broad surcingle. The howdah slipped backward, the passengers screamed, and jumped and slid off. Nobody was hurt, although a stout lady nearly crushed the keeper as she dropped to the ground, shouting for him to catch her. With such antics chalked up against this elephant, we were disturbed to get a call from the watchman, before dawn, that she had broken out of her stall and was roaming somewhere around the Park. It was the dead of winter with deep snow on the ground. There had been a heavy rain during the night, with a sudden change to cold. The surface of the snow carried a thick ice-crust; the Park paths were like glass. What conditions for a roaming elephant!

In the hours before the dawn it was difficult to assemble the keepers, with an automobile cutting dizzy capers on glazed roadways. When the first men arrived they witnessed an astonishing spectacle; they swung their lanterns, rubbed their eyes and scarcely believed it.

By deduction they were able to piece together the order of events. Alice's stall was flooded up to the rim of the coping. Icy-cold water had backed from the sewer through the floor drain, possibly because the rain in the yards was blocked from the storm sewers by the ice. There were fully eight inches of water in the stall, which would be ankle-deep for an elephant.

In summer Alice is fond of standing in a puddle, but the flooding of her stall with icy water was another matter. Even with her inch-thick hide, she soon suffered from cold feet. She started an attack upon the great doors. They had withstood former onslaughts, but failed to endure this protracted battering. One after another, the massive bolts were bent. With a rattling and a loosening of the fastenings, the charging continued and a door flew open. Alice squeezed out and stepped into her yard, without knowing the treacherous condition of the ground. From lines of deep scratches on the slanting ice, it appeared that she must have slid all the way to the yard gate in one majestic, skiing sweep.

Now her impetuous nature was aroused. The gate was closed, but not chained. She knew all about the bar that held the gate—and easily slid it back and emerged into the Park, her gait like the gyrations of a novice at skating. It was at this moment that the watchman coming up from the south section of the Park saw the slipping bulk against the dim background of snow and ice, and he, in turn, slipped and slid to a telephone.

The marks on the ice showed Alice's trail. Once she fell down, as was evidenced by two bent fence posts and many scratches. Her progress led toward the service yards and here, I think, is verification of the belief that an elephant's memory is long. Years before she had visited that yard and the cook had handed her a loaf of bread as she went by the bins. Her tracks led to the bread bin, the top of which she had wrenched open. She had fared poorly, since there were not more than half a dozen loaves—a depressing scarcity after the slipping journey. In the breaking dawn she discovered the big bins for temporary dumping of waste paper, peanut and popcorn boxes, and she scattered these containers to the four winds when she found that they were all empty.

Now it dawned upon Alice that she was having a miserable time. The cold was penetrating her thick skin, the footing was awful—she would return to the elephant house.

On the way back she resented the whole affair. It had first been a case of cold feet; now she was cold all over. To ease her feelings she swung her trunk at the paper cans along the path and knocked them right and left. But at last she reached the elephant house, and the open gate leading to her stall. For years she had gazed at visitors strolling about on a spacious floor. That was the place. There wouldn't be any water there.

The obstacle standing in Alice's way was the size of the doors. They were built for humans, not elephants, to go through. Besides, there was a storm vestibule. But Alice felt this to be a time for vigorous exercise. The vestibule was demolished, and then the frame and transom leading into the building. She entered the spacious, heated structure. The exercise had made her feel better, but she was still a bit chilled, so she tore down fifty feet of netting extending upward from the visitors' rails.

What astonished the arriving keepers was the spectacle of Alice, lolling against a big radiator on the main floor of the elephant house. She greeted the men with her usual little grunts and squeals. The only indisposition from the escapade was our own headache as we repaired the damage. Alice developed not so much as a sniffle from her winter night's walk.

With a collection of about three thousand specimens, mammals, birds and reptiles, and approximately three million visitors coming to see them annually, the records show no injury to a visitor, man, woman or child, from an escaped animal during the close to forty years' history of the institution. Does the public realize our vigilance in this direction? There are hundreds of fastenings; there is the responsibility of everyone from keepers to heads of departments. I often envy the curators of museums, where everything is "stuffed," or mounted in glass cases. Their day's work may be hard, but it is tranquil; the sound of a telephone at night comes without a shock.

Chapter IX

A QUIET NIGHT

The head-keeper hailed me as I came in from lunch.

"Those solenodons just came in from Haiti."

Going into the receiving room I saw a dingy-looking box with a slatted top—but what prizes it contained! One of the fascinations of the study of zoölogy is that there is always something new to be learned, and no more fascinating subjects for animal observations could be imagined than solenodons. These creatures are unchanged hangovers from dim periods millions of years ago, when Nature tried out the first warm-blooded, four-legged animals or mammals—a series of misfits unsuited to survive long. The fossils of these ancient types were encased in rock strata, except the solenodon and a few other small types widely scattered over the world. Why had these uncouth remnants survived? They were alleged to be "stupid" and of eccentric habits. With this background, the small creatures noisily scratching in that slatted box were fine problems for a study of feeding and habits.

The solenodons were no larger than a guinea pig,

with stout body, but movable nose of such length that in proportion to the size of the animal it might be compared with half the length of an elephant's trunk. The eyes were very small and beady, the claws long and powerful for digging. These specimens had arrived during the cold weather and the supply of grubs sent along with them from the tropics was not enough to last a week. Since no additional insects could be obtained unless they were ordered from Florida, and that would take too long, we experimented with scraped beef mixed with white of egg.

My experience with those small animals was unusual. I feared that they might be extremely delicate as captives, but we have to be prepared to take special care of such specimens when we order them. They took the beef and egg diet sparingly; then I found that they liked plain meat much better. I tried them with freshly killed sparrows, with which the Park is infested. These they devoured voraciously. When warm weather returned and insects were abundant, they no longer cared for them, and continued to thrive on a diet of sparrows and beef, and to be contented as captives. It is possible that their adaptability has kept them extant through the ages.

Not only does the zoölogist get a kick from contacts with the stranger members of the animal world, the visitor to the zoo also gains an insight into the significance of various kinds of life. A descriptive label on the solenodons' cage tells the story—that in the distant past at the close of the age of giant reptiles or dinosaurs, the first primitive mammals appeared and were forms directly related to the solenodon, unique in structure of skeleton and teeth, and that a close ally with similarly pointed nose still survives on the other side of the earth, in Madagascar.

Such are the prize packages that keep coming to a zoölogical collection. There is always something to anticipate—something for which to wait eagerly.

A pair of lesser pandas from Tibet gave me more concern than the dietary problem of the solenodons. The pandas were particularly attractive, somewhat like raccoons, except for the tail, which was longer and more luxuriant in its reddish hair than the brush of a fox. These animals were very difficult to obtain. They looked like flesh-eaters, but would not touch meat, and continued to eat a breakfast food, rather tasteless to my mind, and, in addition, a few white grapes. Yet they appeared in good pelage and spirits. For such types we were beginning to experiment with small tablets alleged to contain concentrated vitamins and the like, though visible quantities of cod-liver oil are more convincing to me. However, Mrs. Grace Olive Wiley had told me that she fed a group of languishing mambas with dead mice into the body cavity of which a tablet supposedly packed with the whole alphabet of vitamins had been injected, and that the appetites of her temperamental snakes picked up, and in a few weeks they were in blooming health.

Solenodon. This small Haitian animal, another of Cuba, and two in distant Madagascar are scientifically declared to be hang-overs from millions of years ago in the days of the dinosaurs. At that remote time Nature tried out the first experiments in warm-blooded animals—an odd lot of misfits.

The African hyrax, which looks like a guinea pig, represents a prehistoric race. Scientists point to it as a descendant from the anything but inspiring types whence the hippopotami were derived. In miniature, its tusks are like those of a hippopotamus.

As remnants of the prehistoric, the armadillos, with the exception of one species, have shrunk to the length of a man's hat.

The giant armadillo. From a world once populous with huge, lumbering armadillos, there has remained a fair-sized sample—six feet long, including length of tail.

Such experiences and studies leave one strongly convinced of the value and interest of a living zoölogical collection. But an outsider sometimes debates that point of view, as is illustrated by a talk which I had with a friend at my home.

Shortly after the bear hunt I was stretched in a lawn chair after dinner practically in a coma. I intended to take a nap, and then get to work on the notes for a scientific article which I was behind schedule in preparing. I heaved a sigh at the crackle of tires on the drive. When an old friend got out of the car, I knew that there would be no work that night. Still, I was glad to see him; there would be other evenings for work.

My visitor was a business man, intensely practical according to the standards of that fraternity. He had once gone on a trip with me, and had had much to say about the vagaries of scientists in doing things, their wastefulness of time, and lack of system. In former writings I have referred to him with considerable satire, and in thinly disguised terms, but he had only laughed uproariously at these references. His point of view on life and mine may be of interest to the reader as illustrations of varying human psychology.

We have had many verbal battles and yet have remained good friends. He doesn't believe in zoos and thinks museums of natural history should be radically changed. Since the advent of miniature groups in the latter, he has become enthusiastic and has given funds for their elaboration in the larger institutions. He declares that he gets the same feeling in looking at them as from peering into the lens of an old-fashioned sugar Easter-egg, and insists that, if you are going to sell an idea in natural history to children, you must study their psychology and go about it in a practical way. Besides, he argues, you can have miniature panoramas of a whole continent represented in the space taken up by one life-sized group of mounted animals. His objection to zoos comes from the cost of feeding the animals. A dead one, he declares, is just as interesting to look at.

"I see you're in a jam," was his greeting.

"What about?"

"Shooting that bear. Haven't you seen the letters in the papers?"

By way of reply, I spoke of the dangerous character of bear psychology; the conditions of the hunt, and then, to talk of something he would consider practical, I mentioned the bear's purchase price of one hundred and fifty dollars as against possible law suits. This made a fair hit.

"At the same time," he argued, "a stuffed bear in a museum would not have given you that trouble, and its maintenance would have been a handful of camphor balls."

It was getting chilly and we went inside, up to my library, where one side of the room is fitted up with the panels of weather instruments, and here the argument continued. I contended that zoos and museums were useful in teaching natural history, and that the term "zoo" was really a weak one, for such education brought vivid realization of the many forms of life, and a reverence for them.

"A reverence for cobras, crocodiles, and man-eating tigers," he snorted.

"Don't interrupt. That's no point at all."

I then emphasized the popularity of the zoo in the Bronx, with its approximately three million visitors each year, and told him how new zoos were springing up all over the country, most of them sponsored by scientific societies. I told him that attendance everywhere was heavy, that public schools were sending children to such places by the class-load. I pointed out the usefulness of maps, charts, and labels telling about the animals; I showed how the zoos and museums visualized the evolution of the living animal from the legions of monsters and grotesque creatures of millions of years ago; how their fossils now chiselled from the rocks were carefully assembled in museums; how such animals as elephants, rhinos and tapirs remained like ghosts of times long past, scant remnants of types that once had wandered all over North America and Europe; also how the llamas of South America were surviving vestiges of races of large and small camels, former inhabitants of what is now the United States; how modern reptiles are but miniatures descended from ancient dinosaurs; how in the zoo, the last survivors, the final link in the tremendous history of the dead still lives and breathes; how there is fascination in looking upon the living form; and how without a doubt, in time the zoos would maintain animals extinct in a wild state—swept by hunting and encroaching civilization from what was once their undisputed domain.

Then again—for I knew how anything "practical" hit my listener—I went into detail about our experiments with the breeding and feeding of hoofed animals, which dovetailed into the science of the development of domestic animals, since the result of our mixing the blood of wild races with domestic was the production of hybrids of value to mankind. I spoke of studies on the longevity and life history of the smaller kinds which were destructive to agriculture or carried diseases to man. I told him how a knowledge of the life cycle of vampire bats (a colony of which I had maintained and studied for over two years) was important in reducing their numbers in the tropics where they had piled up an appalling record in the transmission of paralytic rabies in cattle and trypanosome infection among horses—among human beings, also, stricken by their bites.

"Confound it," and I banged the table, "you won't give credit to what goes on in a modern zoo. They are not menageries any more. To keep impressive exhibits before the public there are diet kitchens, hospitals, and pathological laboratories."

By this time he had slipped down in my biggest chair, with his feet on another. He looked at me quizzically. But I was now warmed up to my subject. To give him an idea of the development in observation and study from the stereotype collections of the old menageries, I told him about an incident which had come up for discussion during a luncheon of the Park staff of officers, and the trail of curious points attending it. I had been keenly interested, although it was outside of the work of my departments.

It had started with an explanation from Lee Crandall, Curator of the Bird Department. He looked tired and said that he had just come up from the docks in his car with a rare humming bird from South America. The diners were interested to hear about this novelty, but only really pricked up their ears when the curator explained that he had had to stop every ten minutes to feed the bird, that longer periods would have brought about exhaustion from lack of food. Since my knowledge of humming birds was limited to admiring their hovering flight, with blurred wings and flashing colors, I asked Crandall if this was a young bird, that it required such frequent feeding.

He told us that humming birds, owing to the constant and rapid motion of their wings, burn up energy at such a rate that they must feed every few minutes. When they are not being shaken up in a car, it is not difficult to feed them in captivity, for small glass receptacles are used, with a laterally projecting tube on the side into which the bird can introduce its long, slender, hollow tongue (somewhat like a suction tube) and draw out the sweet and nourishing fluid mixture. Recently large humming-bird enclosures of glass, with a profusion of plants and bright flowers have been installed in several of the larger zoos. The technique in maintaining these birds has been brought to a high degree of efficiency. In a recent communication from the St. Louis Zoo it is stated that the humming-bird cage continues to be the most popular exhibit in the bird house. Concealed electric radiators under thermostatic control maintain the tropical exhibit at an even temperature of ninety degrees, even in winter weather. The report further stated:

"Observation has taught us many things about the humming birds. Each bird feeds on the average of every three minutes, and each bird empties about four of the feeding tubes each day. They will not drink water unless they can lap it off a leaf, so a leafy branch is so placed that water from the spray falls on it constantly. The birds also come to this branch to bathe, and seem to get much enjoyment out of the soft spray falling on their feathers. They are very fond of the fruit flies which are raised for them, and the popping of their beaks can be distinctly heard as they pursue a tiny fly across the cage."

Later I learned that, considering the humming bird's need of constantly adding food-fuel to balance its constant play of muscular activity, the scintillating specimen in our Park must be kept especially busy, for the head-keeper in the bird department found unmistakable evidence that this bird harbored a tapeworm. A parasitologist might wonder whether such an environment was favorable for a tapeworm, or not.

Another point about humming birds in relation to

their feeding habits bothered me—their migration. Each autumn, they made their way thousands of miles from the North to the South. How could these tiny animate engines, that burn up fuel in a few minutes, tackle a trip like that? I spoke to some ornithologists about this, and they shrugged their shoulders. They could only hazard a guess that the speed of the humming bird was exceedingly rapid. But even at that, I argued, a flight of a thousand miles or more would be a question of hours. Visiting the ground every few minutes to replenish food-fuel for wing beats at a blur seemed highly improbable.

A hint of the answer to my questions came shortly afterward in a front page article that appeared in the *New York Times* on October 28, 1936. It was in the form of an Associated Press dispatch from Williams Lake in British Columbia, and read:

> "A hunter's shot that killed a Canada goose also killed a passenger—a humming bird traveling southward, nestled in the soft warm feathers of the larger bird. Ornithologists say it is common for humming birds to stow away, and frequently when geese are brought down, the small creatures dart away from their crashing air liner."

I told my scientific friends about this dispatch and they were amused.

"What do you say when you're asked about beavers dragging loads of mud on their flat tails, whether there are hoop snakes, and whether rattlers commit suicide?" they countered.

I replied that such allegations were known to be myths.

"Well," one of my associates remarked, "that is what we think about large birds carrying the smaller species on migration trips."

As a sort of parallel incident I cited an experience with a llama during sub-zero weather. The animal had been lying down. As I approached it, it rose and trotted off a few yards, then gave itself a vigorous shake. Several rats fell out of its luxuriant coat, but I saw a heaving of its pelage showing that one of the rodents had hung on. Here was association and toleration among the large and the small. Still my scientific friends remained cold to the thought of small bird transportation by larger birds.

I had told these stories to arouse my visitor's interest in zoos. Then I paused to get his reaction.

"Humph," was his only response; still he was staring at a pattern of the rug, and I figured the argument had gone over.

Finally he turned. "You mentioned several practical things. You found that in two years vampires refused everything but blood, which shows that those devilish things seek blood of man and beast, and your work in the tropics to reduce their numbers is worth time and money. You've done good work with snake poisons in finding remedies for bites and in using the diluted poison itself in human troubles. Conserving the life of man and domestic beasts seems to me to be one of the important jobs of the future."

"I'll give you a jolt—something to think about," I replied. "That is the general idea, in studies of modern biological science, but let me tell you about a medical meeting I recently attended. I was at a table with several elderly men in close contact with each other's work and prominent in their fields. They were talking about bacteriology, and the progress in combating forms of germ life. They spoke about checking neutralizing measures in combating hitherto unconquerable diseases. Other measures were in sight.

" 'Gentlemen,' remarked one of the men, 'such will ever be our course in research. The death rate from disease will be greatly reduced from the present. Future generations of doctors will receive greater acclaim in this work, but actually it amounts to a great interference: it is unnatural and will ultimately lead to a terrible problem of the deterioration of the human race by overpopulation of the earth. Human beings should be dying normally of the natural causes necessary to keep the species under control!'

"What do you think of that?" was my query.

"Terrible. Those men should have been spanked. What were you doing at a medical meeting?"

"There was to be a discussion about the detection of ultra-microscopic organisms in filterable virus. A filterable virus you know is——"

My listener snorted. "That's what I've always told you. You jump mentally from one spot to another. Look at all of this." He pointed to the panel of weather instruments on the wall. "Where does this get you? Between clocks to wind and graphs to change and adjusting these electrical gadgets, you burn up a lot of time!" He was referring to an enthusiasm of mine discussed in the next chapter.

Our conversation was winding up, as it usually did, in a battle.

I have been listening to this criticism on and off for years from friends, and others inclined to satire. My father had said the same thing, aghast at the variety of my interests. "Burn up a lot of time," was the withering comment. But the time was not "burned up," it was time I enjoyed; time in which I was absorbed; time that deepened understanding as life went on.

In connection with my varied activities, my friend might have been interested and critical about what happened a few days later in a radio studio.

"What do you mean by this climax?" stormed the dramatic director.

I looked at him in surprise. I was reading my part in a radio script—and I thought I was doing well, because I was being natural.

Here I was transgressing again. I was taking time out from my scientific life, but when a man has been traveling and making new observations he gets requests from the studios to say something. So I have been called upon to be actor, recitationist, and book reviewer, and my time on the air has run anywhere from four minutes to half an hour.

But to make clear why the dramatic director exploded, I must give the background which led up to it.

One of the big advertising companies had asked me to write some sketches about my experiences with animals. I had done so, and the sketch I was at the moment rehearsing was an experience I had had in Central America. A friend of mine from the States who had had no jungle experience but wanted some was with me in a small automobile which was fighting its way through a trail cut for the hauling of mahogany. It was getting dark; we had dropped into a mud hole, and twisted the front springs. I suggested that we build a small fire for light, unloosen the spring saddle, and hammer the leaves back into place. It was ten miles to getting "out," and that meant a dirty little village of thatched houses, but to my friend, that settlement was a haven for repose of mind. Tangles of lianas and a forest floor on each side of us of moldy debris, knee deep in spots, was not to his liking in the fast settling dusk of the tropics.

We finally got the fire built although my companion had been terrified at every step to pick up a stick lest it should turn out to be a snake. Then we heard a rustling at one side.

"What's that," he whispered, following the dialogue of the script.

"I don't know," was my reply. "Loosen those two nuts. We want to get out of here—these mosquitoes are bad."

"There are jaguars around here," whispered my friend. "Didn't we hear that one killed a donkey!" My "friend," it should be explained, was impersonated by a professional actor of the studio staff. His remark about jaguars was delivered with emotional intensity.

The script led on to my stopping and listening, for a sound like a sizable animal coming through the jungle warrants attention.

"Stand steady," I remarked quietly.

It was here that the dramatic director got red in the face and when the script later revealed that it was only a harmless armadillo floundering through dead leaves and ambling across the trail, he blew up.

"You acted as if you had no more interest in what was coming than if it had been a mouse," he raved. "Why didn't both of you jump for your guns. Your remarks should have been loud and excited."

I told him that at the time we had not had guns, except for a revolver under one of the seat cushions, and I saw no reason to get excited about something that might have been a stray hog. Jaguars, as a matter of fact, didn't prowl through the jungle with a noise like that—and, if you came across one, it was likely to turn a somersault to get out of your way. I was merely trying to be casual and humorous, I explained, to allay the fears of my friend.

That sketch went flat in the studio, although to me it gave some good sidelights. And so the director gave me a bawling out because I failed to yell and get excited.

Downstairs in a sumptuous room, where the audition was "piped" in by a loud-speaker and went nowhere else, was the advertising staff of a nationally known corporation, who wanted pep in their programs. I had no intention of providing the desired pep while I made a fool of myself and I so informed the director. When we parted company I think he was convinced that I could be as hard-boiled as he had been, and despite his proffered politeness, I refrained from hand-shaking and walked out.

The actor, well known on the air, walked out with me. He was in accord with my attitude, and declared that I had been right. If I had behaved as that director wanted me to, I would have been branded by most of the radio audience, if the sketch had been broadcast, as an unfit and hysterical custodian of a collection of dangerous animals. So that was that, with the sketch turned down flat.

Various broadcasts, where I have had my way, sometimes in the guise of acting, have been accounted successful and a generous inflow of letters has attested to the fact.

I have no objection to sketches, so long as they are truthfully worked out, and I have noticed that radio is gradually toning down to painstaking portrayals;

that the too snappy directors of the past are giving way to a type more interested in authenticity.

At a recent audition I noticed the extraordinary pains taken to give a meticulously accurate background. If the audience could have seen what was happening in the studio, it would have been more entertained than it was from hearing the sketch.

Before the rehearsal I chatted with the sound-effect technicians. The conversation reverted to an early sketch when the effect to be carried over had been that of ice clinking in a tall glass at a club conference. Various experiments had been tried, including the lowering of a chain into a tumbler. In the midst of these trials, an announcer came into the studio and suggested mixing up a tall drink and clinking the ice in the glass. And so that problem was solved very simply. But now, I have been told, the invention of cellophane has been a boon to the studios, for by crackling it in front of the microphone, the frying of eggs, or sputtering bacon in the pack can of a cowboy on the range, can be duplicated exactly. But on the whole, sound effects in the radio studio, as I have observed them, are becoming very complicated.

A thrilling example was given in the studio, where I was to give a broadcast about elephants. I was to give a talk, pepping up to a climax when an elephant, after being weighed, tried to break through my office door. The visit was fairly friendly, but exciting, since the animal got stuck in the door frame. Here, I felt, I could speak out, for elephants are not accustomed to polite conversation. My part was satisfactory to the dramatic director, but as the program ran into a half hour, another episode was injected, and here came the complication.

Two actors had been engaged. In the sketch an elephant was suddenly to appear on a railroad track in South Africa as the train rounded a curve. I had written the sketch and it allowed, very properly, for plenty of excitement.

We assembled an hour and a half before the broadcast and rushed through the script to see what was wanted in the shape of sound effects. My part was simple; the sketch as I had worked it out was accepted in toto. Several sound effects, none of them difficult, were decided upon. The idea of an elephant bucking a train, however, called for more elaboration, and the sound-effect men were sent for accessories. They came back wheeling an apparatus that looked like a grand piano. Mounted in the top were three phonograph turntables, while various drawers carried utensils and appliances of mysterious shapes. I was informed that this rolling unit was capable of producing many kinds of noises such as the chugging of trains, the rumbling of wheels on rails, and the like. The operator of the cabinet laid out a series of utensils. But there were more to come. A compressed air tank was wheeled in and a whistle attached. Then came a huge sheet of heavy metal as big as a fair-sized rug. This was followed by someone rolling in what looked like an ash can full of stones. These were dumped on the metal plate. Another assistant arrived with a coal shovel. One of the technicians started scooping up the stones on the plate. I got the idea at once. This was to indicate shovelling coal into the locomotive boiler, but there was no place to shoot it. The condition was remedied by sending for a tarpaulin and sliding the stones onto this deadening material.

It was astonishing how fast the preparation for the background sounds was built up. Within ten minutes we were surrounded by activity, but trouble arose. What was to imitate the clanging of the boiler door after the engine had been fired? The director scratched his head, but only for five seconds.

"Bring in that jail door we had made up last week," he commanded.

Within five minutes the front of a jail appeared in the studio. The barred gate clanged noisily.

"O.K.," said the director.

But a major item was still to be settled—the sound of the collision between the elephant and the train.

I thought this would take a lot of time, but it didn't. Somebody staggered in with a high column of empty peach baskets and someone else with six feet of heavy chain. As an experiment two peach baskets were placed in front of a chair and an assistant, with particularly large feet, was told to jump on them simultaneously when the word was given. That word was also to control the dropping of the chain on the metal plate—all of this to be accompanied by sounds from the cabinet, which included escaping steam.

Before I could realize that things could happen so quickly, there was a leap from the chair, the chain fell and pandemonium broke loose from the cabinet.

"O.K.," said the director. "Rehearsal."

We went through the whole thing, which timed satisfactorily and ended with the studio looking like a wreck, with broken baskets and stones that had overshot the tarpaulin.

"Swell," said the director, but there was an argument about the dialogue between the engineer and fireman when they sighted the big elephant on the track.

The script read: "Holy cats" (from the engineer).

The fireman simply yelled, "An elephant!"

There was debate as to whether a British engineer in Africa, would say "Holy cats!" The contention was that it didn't sound like a British engineer. Someone suggested "Blime me eye," but this caused a debate as to whether a British cockney would be driving a locomotive in South Africa. A voice chimed in that the engineer might be a Boer and speak in Transvaal dialect. Then it was suggested that, inasmuch as American jazz was played all over the world even to the Fiji Islands, "Holy cats!" might be considered a cosmopolitan expression, and that it had the additional advantage of being short and not blasphemous.

The script was rendered without an error, and I waded through wreckage as I left the studio, while a gang of cleaners appeared to put a beautiful taupe carpet back in condition for orchestras and the like.

By the grape vine, I have heard that sponsors are afraid to put me on the air because I have had a lot to do with snakes, and they fear that to a radio audience, even though I am talking about four-legged animals, I might call up a sinister background. I have had records cut during auditions and broadcasts, and in my laboratory is a turntable and amplifier. A record that was cut at the time of the elephant episode has been played many times and the volume control is always turned to the top notch at the impact of the engine with the elephant.

In this connection, let me say that the science of cutting disks to file as records of spoken addresses has progressed to a high state of perfection. Whereas with the old-time phonograph records, the cutting was about thirty lines to an inch and the duration of a record but a very few minutes, it is now possible to cut as many as two hundred lines to an inch and such records play fifteen minutes or more. These records are played by an electric "pick-up" arm, delicately balanced and amplified by radio tubes. Needle hiss of the past has been eliminated and the clarity of these records matches every tone and inflection of the human voice. Also, the machines may be wired to radio loud speakers even when remotely situated from the transmitting apparatus.

Such an outfit in my laboratory has convinced my friends that a scientist can do useful things in addition to his writings and general lectures. I have made a series of readings for the blind from my books of adventures and from work on various problems presented in untechnical terms. The voice of the author gives a cordial touch by expressing his sympathetic interest. Quite recently I filed a row of records covering the reading of an entire book. From the letters received from the blind, I know that these readings are keenly appreciated. They give me more pleasure than testimonials from scientific institutions.

Chapter X

HURRICANE

Returning in the late autumn from a trip to Cuba, I was engaged in mental activities which gave me a furtive feeling that I was doing wrong; yet I decided to go ahead. There was a scientific job to be tackled and work to do in the movie studio which loomed as obstacles to what I had in mind. I was determined to construct a remote control weather bureau—that is, to build a set of instruments to be placed on a platform at the top of the house and to run multiple wires into my library where everything that was going on with the weather would be recorded in lights.

The idea was born in Havana. It started during a talk with Colonel Bicknell of the International Telephone and Telegraph Company, who had discussed with me an electric wind vane. Extra details flocked together after I visited the meteorological observatory atop Belén University, where the instruments are presided over by Father Mariano Guiterrez Lanza, the well-known watcher of hurricanes.

The ideas accumulated at Havana formed a new outlet for energy. At home, across my writing table, my wife regarded me with a quizzical stare.

"And what are the diagrams that look like veins and arteries?" she asked.

"The multiple wiring for the new instruments."

"Won't they be very costly?"

"I'm going to make them."

"How about the work in the studio?"

There was no answer to that. There followed hectic sessions in the studio, with late hours. The work was done and it was thoroughly done, and the arterial diagrams again appeared on the writing table.

After a week at my tool bench engraving a panel of bakelite in the sixteen major segments of the compass, boring for miniature lamp ports at the outside margins, setting the panel in a brass frame and preparing the complicated back to receive the multiple wire leads from the base of the wind vane, a feeling stole over me akin to the feeling of guilt in a dream of walking along Broadway in a bathing suit. The atmosphere of the tool bench seemed just as inappropriate. My place was at the writing table on that scientific job, and with a sigh I cleaned up the place, leaned the panel against the back of the bench, looked it over several times in commendation—and tackled the scientific job. When that was done I felt like a boy out of school. I think that it is these alternations in jobs that makes me look back on a life filled with pleasurable interests.

For two months the tool bench lights burned until

all hours. I built a wind vane with double tails to international specifications, and two anemometers, one with hollow cups to register wind speed according to government standards and another following an idea suggested in Havana. An opening was cut in the roof, a stairway built and the instruments mounted. The vane had a segmented commutator at the base corresponding to the segments of the engraved panel. A commutator arm made contact according to the point of the wind. Conduits carried vari-colored "telltale" wires to the panels in my library and a heavy storage battery furnished the current for the system.

When all was finished, I made the following installation which, I thought, looked very handsome: a panel two feet square indicating the face of the compass, with a light burning at the segment from which the wind was pointing; an anemometer making contact and flashing a light every twenty-five revolutions to show the speed of the wind according to official standards; a larger hollow-cup anemometer expanding the arms of a governor and showing the speed of wind along an engraved brass plate marked in miles per hour, and the Beaufort scale as figured at sea. On one side of the mountings was a baragraph, which set me back a hundred dollars, and on the other a microbarograph. Outside the window was a thermograph with a light playing on it. In addition, there was a cabinet with a set of large albums for the weekly posting of thermograms, barograms and other records.

Similar in appearance, both the two-toed and the three-toed sloths are leaf-eaters. As captives they are markedly different. The two-toed species lives for years, while the three-toed kind survives but a few months.

Guidance to a scientist's outdoor work. A plant of electrified panels connected with wind vane and anemometers. Among the instruments portraying the pulse of the weather are a barograph, a hygrometer, and a "piped-in" thermometer. The ceiling compass shows correction from declination occurring near New York.

One of my business friends who first saw the installation and heard how long I had taken to build it, said I was a "nut." I have noticed, however, that he and others stick around that room in keen interest; my seafaring and aeronautical friends think it is great, and one quite important steamer has duplicated the outfit.

"It's unusual," said a visitor, "for an animal man to have no trophies and stuffed things to remind him of the chase."

I told him I didn't like dead things and he said, "How about all the mechanical contrivances?"

"Well," was my rejoinder, "that's the pulse of the weather. There's something happening among those lights, isn't there?"

There was one humorous incident connected with my construction of the weather station, and that was concerned with my old friend Andy, who had been my electrician in the early days of the movie studio. Andy was then freckled and precocious, a wizard with the "juice" and always tearing the apparatus to pieces to make it better—with success. He is now a chief electrician. He taught me more about electricity than I could have learned in a technical school. We keep in touch, sending Christmas greetings and occasional post cards while traveling. I wrote Andy for advice about the multiple wiring.

He answered that, if I would wait until spring with the installation, he would take a couple of weeks off, come East, and help me build it. The letter gave me a shock. I knew exactly what would happen if Andy took charge. I would be thrust aside and he would take hold, in his speed of weird competence comprehending technicalities at a glance and scorning diagrams. It was the slow completion of the details of my drawings that made the job a joy. Andy would have taken the kick out of it. I can see his smile when he reads this.

To observe and study the weather is a fine diversion and I recommend it for a boy. It will mean much that is interesting in later life and the knowledge acquired may be of high practical value. It has been of great use to me, though at first it was prompted only by interest. Intensive study and observation in later years have been of great value in my outdoor work.

People ask me when I first became interested in this and that; when I was first interested in snakes, for instance. My first recollection of that particular interest brings back a picture of a cat-tail marsh near Gravesend Bay—behind Brooklyn. My parents were spending the summer there, and the marsh attracted me during my boyish wanderings. I could work out a trail where the cat-tails had toppled and formed a mat-like surface, and there I spotted a pair of garter snakes. They glided out of sight, but day after day I went to the spot and saw them again and again. I was twelve years old and I longed to possess those snakes, but when I mentioned them to my parents there was such consternation that owning the snakes then seemed as impossible as owning a couple of lions.

My interest in the weather developed shortly after this, although from early childhood I had loved snowstorms, and felt depressed when a storm was over. I watched the sky for a smudge of thunderstorms and liked to hear the wind blow. But the first definite thought of observing the weather came, I remember, during a walk down Seventh Avenue, in Harlem, when I was about fourteen years old. It was in the afternoon. The morning had been fairly clear, but a sheet of filmy cloud was dimming the sun. Faintly definable in the veil were streaks of darker gray. They came out of the southwest. The western edge of this encroaching cloud sheet could be seen low down, in the northwest. The picture is as clear as if it had happened yesterday.

The reason for this is probably the fact that I made mental predictions at the time—and they worked out. I had seen that hazy, streaky kind of cloud before. If it spread out of the southwest in winter there would be a northeast wind and a snowstorm; but if it ran parallel with the northwestern horizon, it would either clear by morning or there wouldn't be much of a snowstorm. My idea was to watch the wind vane on Quinn's Livery Stable when I got home, and the gilded horse on its flagpole became an object of daily inspection. At the time I didn't know any specific name for that cloud sheet or anything about storm tracks. If I had, those directional streaks of a classified cloud formation would have meant a great deal more than mere supposition.

Just before the darkness of supper time, the vane had worked around toward the north, but I had seen it do that before and come back to its average clearweather point of northwest.

After supper I strolled over to 125th Street, where the glare from the arc lamps shone upon the gilded horse on the livery stable flagpole. The gritty dust was picked up by a gathering wind. The head of the horse was pointed to a four-way sector beneath the vane bearing the gilt letters NE. Even before I was out of bed the next morning, I noticed that the sound of wheels in the street was muffled. A heavy snow was falling.

It was not long after this incident that I saw announced among lectures in the American Museum auditorium two talks on the weather. One was announced as "Cloud Formations and Their Significance." The other was "Storm Tracks of the Northern Hemisphere." I attended both and learned a lot, while an elderly speaker discoursed to a sparsely occupied room. The formation of my hazy cloud was known as cirrus. When it appeared as an indefinable veil, it was known as cirro-nebulus, which indicated the approach of an intense storm or cyclone. I was still in the air as to the definition of a cyclone, though it sounded formidable enough. Various other clouds, which I remembered having seen, were projected on the screen from lantern slides. The lecture ended with mild applause and I left with the idea that cirrus was associated with storms, that a lot of other clouds didn't mean much, and that I must get a chart on cloud formations, which the lecturer had said could be obtained from Washington.

The second lecture, a week later, was more sparsely attended than the first, yet to me it was more interesting, because the speaker explained in simple terms how different kinds of weather come into being.

The "weather" as defined by the layman, he said, is produced by a series of great inverted waves of atmospheric pressure and the deep valleys between them. The crests point toward the earth from above. Over the greater part of the year, they roll along like swells on an enormous sea. From edge to edge these atmospheric waves may be a thousand miles or more in breadth—and the valleys between them equally wide. The troughs or "depressions" as a rule are of lesser magnitude. The general movement of atmospheric waves is from west to east. Their average rate of travel across the United States is a thousand miles a day. Their passage is indicated by pressure of the crest of the waves and the fall, showing the valley between them. It is within the inverted valley that the storms occur and if the trough is deep, the storm is severe.

With a barometer in the home and by comparing its actions with the daily weather map in several of the newspapers, the significance of the "Highs" (the atmospheric waves) and the "Lows" (the storm areas) could be readily seen. At this point I told myself that in some way I must get a barometer.

Two other points were to be noted, the lecturer explained. One was the tendency of weather formations to be circular, particularly the more intense storm areas.

The second point related to wind movement about them —clockwise with the "Highs" and counterclockwise around the "Lows." With the former, the air flowed downward and outward, then around the area. The winds flowed toward the storm areas, then around them. Hence a storm to the north would cause a southerly wind, flowing toward it to fill the depression.

After the lecture I diffidently made my way up front where a few people were asking questions. I had two questions I had long wanted to ask, with nobody to turn to. Edging toward the lecturer I found myself facing him. He looked at me tolerantly.

"Sir," I said, "the wind blows northeast with heavy snowstorms. Would that mean that they come from the south?"

"Not all weather movements are from west to east," was his answer. "Your 'heavy' snowstorm usually comes from the Gulf of Mexico or up the Atlantic coast, and in these latitudes turns easterly into the ocean area. Cold winds from the north flow into it when it approaches this section. New York may have a foot of snow that a few days before was dense clouds over a tropical ocean."

The adult interrogators were filtering away; the lecturer gathered his notes from under the reading lamp and walked toward the aisle. I was close at his heels, for my remaining and more important question was still to be asked.

Keeping up with his long-legged stride, I sought respectfully to slow him down.

"I attended your first lecture," I stammered.

He kept right on, but it was a long walk through the Museum hall. I had hopes.

"You are keen about the weather?" he asked.

"Yes, sir. Your lectures have shown me a great deal about what it means."

We were passing the middle of the long hallway.

"May I ask, sir, why the wind goes northeast when bars of cirrus are oblique with the northwestern horizon, and doesn't work around much, and it clears if cirrus runs straight along that horizon?"

The question and the fast gait left me breathless.

"Now that is a sensible question," said the lecturer, stopping. "When bars of approaching cirrus cloud run parallel to the coast, the center of the storm is usually too far out at sea for us to get its precipitation or note its storm winds. If the cirrus points from the southwest the storm is coming from that direction and part of its center will usually go over the observer. If you are going to be interested in the weather, young man, study the point of cirrus clouds—in winter. In summer, much of the cirrus to be seen means nothing. It drifts off the heads of thunder clouds and is not associated with a storm sheet."

We continued to the lobby and as he was getting on his coat and hat, I edged away to assure him that I had no more questions. To my mind, it would have been an anticlimax and would have spoiled what had happened if more had been added. Nevertheless, as I bade him good night I couldn't resist asking:

"Are there small barometers?"

"You can buy a fair aneroid for about twenty-five dollars," was his discouraging answer. "Subscribe to the *Monthly Weather Review* from the government at Washington."

That evening steered me definitely toward intensive studies of the weather. I considered, at the time, that it might be a long while before I had a barometer. Possibly I might ask for one as a birthday present from my father and for a subscription to the *Monthly Weather Review* from my mother. But remembering the way my father had talked about my varied interests, I finally decided not to ask for a barometer.

Cirrus clouds and northeast winds—in winter—became an absorbing study. From the government magazines I learned that Alaska and the Canadian Yukon formed the breeding place of the severe cold waves of winter. These were areas of cold, down-pressing air which sweep on a curving southeastward track from the northwest, through the central and eastern United States and pass off the Atlantic coast into the ocean. Their formation in the northwestern area and the course they follow were typical of winter conditions.

With the approach of spring the area of origin of the northwestern "Highs" produced fewer of them, and another track was indicated on the weather map. Over this came "Highs," entering the United States from the Pacific, their centers appearing at about the latitude of Washington or Oregon. They contained little cold, since their origin was over ocean waters of mild temperature.

Over the northern tract there then appeared a leisurely procession of depressions, or storms. As their centers moved eastward along the northern boundary, the winds flowed upward from the south toward them. In this way was the warmth of the southern Atlantic and the Gulf of Mexico wafted into a winter-weary country, bringing the first indications of spring. Now and then conditions reverted to formations and movements along the winter tracks.

With accumulated knowledge, the need for a barometer became imperative. Eventually I saved up the money and bought one at a pawnshop. It was soon to give me a thrilling demonstration when again there was my watched-for vision in the sky—the cirrus clouds. But now it was midsummer.

I had learned from the government magazines of the greatest of all storms, rarely reaching the northern coast, but carrying one of Nature's most tremendous manifestations—the hurricane. Unlike storm movements in the northern hemisphere, these overwhelming disturbances frequently formed in the hot seas off the west coast of Africa, moved slowly westward at the rate of about three hundred miles a day, and, after crossing the tropical Atlantic, either swung through the Yucatan Channel and battered the coast of Mexico, or sought to recurve off our eastern coast, and took a northeasterly course across the northern Atlantic to the eastward. After recurving and entering colder waters they generally lost force. If they reached the coast before the sharp recurve, they retained their fury. A fifty-year chart of hurricane tracks reaching the southern coasts from Mexico to Georgia looks like the radiation of missiles discharged from a blunderbuss. Likewise, the recurves off the coast into the Atlantic are radial. "Hits" north of Hatteras are very rare, and New York, in the history of the weather bureau, has taken it on the nose but once, and that was shortly after I bought my barometer, in 1893. Hurricane clouds have been in the sky as storms passed north or northeast over the ocean, and again there have been heavy winds, ugly sky manifestations and torrential rains as such storms passed inland and worked in a northerly direction, inshore from the south. But put the hurricane well ashore and it loses its vigor, which depends upon moisture over warm ocean waters. Vapors flowing in from all sides toward the center of the cyclone give it body to retain its circular swirl over a diameter of a hundred miles or more.

With my love of storms, such manifestations, even the edges of them, were something to watch for, phases of keen interest in the flat weather of midsummer. You may imagine, then, my excitement on the 23rd day of August, 1893, when the newspapers printed items about a hurricane approaching the coast and headed toward New York. My work of setting butterflies' wings at the Museum that morning was intermittent. The Curator of Entomology was irritated by my restlessness.

"Snakes and storms," he grumbled. "You won't have space in your head for your work."

I respectfully refrained from telling him that softening an interminable series of dead butterflies, adjusting their wings on setting boards, and then pinning the tiny locality cards week after week was monotonous for a youth; that on this day I felt like another person. I stepped down the hallway to consult Professor Hovey's barometer. It read 29.80. I resisted the temptation to walk down the long hallway for a look at the southern sky until lunch time.

At noon the sky was white—a cirrus haze, or cirronebulus to be exact. The sun was a patch. Thick cumulus, like lead-colored heads of cauliflower loomed here and there. The air was still, hot and oppressive. I could not refrain from giving a diagnosis of sky classification to the Curator.

"Hurricane, fiddlesticks!" he snorted. "It's hot and we'll probably have a thunder storm."

Later in the afternoon I went up the hallway again to Professor Hovey's office. He was the Curator of Geology and the only member of the staff who appeared even remotely interested in the weather. His barometer still read 29.80.

"These storms usually turn and go out to sea again, Raymond," he said. "There may be nothing more than a northeast blow."

"But, Professor Hovey, the diagrams show that they recurve off an air pressure gradient of 30 or higher.

We're two points under that now." His casual way of speaking cast a damper on my spirits. With a guilty feeling, momentarily expecting a call from my chief, I quickly made the trip to the south windows. The haze was thickening and graying, but no bands were present to form an estimate of the angle with the horizon.

The chief was keen and he sensed just where I had been.

"Fussing around like an old grandmother about the weather," he remarked, not unkindly. "Finish that batch in the softening box. We'll take a trip to the Palisades tomorrow. I'm interested in this rumor about the summer brood of *Orgyia* being heavily parasitized."

The batch of softened butterflies was mounted and I started down town to take the ferry across the bay to South Brooklyn, where the family had moved. In the harbor there was a wide vista of the heavens. The west and south were blue gray, and the east was a procession of wind-torn clouds, moving very fast. During the half-hour trip across the harbor that canopy of scud came nearer; it was getting overhead and there was a misty rain squall. When I arrived home the barometer was 29.70.

After the evening meal the barometer had dropped to 29.60. There was a rustling of leaves, just a mild wind. I went out on the lawn. The wind had swung northeasterly.

I was positive now that this would be the most thrilling northeast wind I had ever seen. The run of scud was coming out of an ENE direction. The storm had not recurved. It was coming toward the coast.

By eight o'clock, the rain squalls had increased to gales and at intervals there was a roar of wind. At midnight I helped my father close the shutters on the upper stories of the north and east sides of the house. Downstairs the glass was heavier. Rain was soon being driven horizontally. Under the swaying arc light outside, it looked like close-set silver wires. But this was only a curtain raiser. The roar increased until it was constant and had a curious effect on the mind, as if it were impossible that the rushing wind could be so relentless, with no lulls, no bracing moments for what was to come. Odd angles of the house, obstructing the pressure, gave off various tones, like an organ out of tune. The arc light outside became a dim patch in rain so torrential that it was driven in around the lower window casings as a spray.

The family stayed up and I watched the storm from a south window, until the house started to rock distinctly.

Going up to my snake room in an uneasy wonder, for the joints of the house were creaking, I gasped at the magnitude of sound. The driven rain sounded like an avalanche crashing on the roof. In my rodent breeding room the rats were running wildly about their cotes, where it was unusual to see more than a couple of pairs at a time. My barometer was down to 29.40, then it dropped a point, then another to 29.20, when at dawn there came a calm which seemed as abrupt as if a whistle cord had been slacked off.

Through the silence came the whimpering and scratching of my fox terrier at the door at the head of the basement steps. I found him crouched on the top stair above three feet of water in the cellar.

Another household incident remains in my mind. During the night my bed "walked" along on its castors to the opposite side of the room.

The blow following the passage of the vortex—when the wind comes on again from the opposite side of such cyclones—was not of hurricane force, since the velocity of such storms is usually slowed down after the advance has gone well inland. However, the reverse or southwest wind was strong enough. Ragged clouds, the color of brick-dust, hurried across the clearing sky.

Managing to reach the ferry to go to the Museum, I saw a state of affairs which I have never witnessed since. No horses were being taken aboard the boat; New York harbor was too rough. As the craft made its way outside, it met a succession of regularly spaced, muddy swells. I can see them yet, strangely symmetrical, precisely alike as they rolled up the harbor. That particular storm recurved and went out to sea again after traversing the land area to southern Labrador where it regained vigor and retained identity, as it moved southeastward, until well east of the Azores—close to the longitude where it had had its origin—and so twice crossed the Atlantic. Its precipitation in the New York area was about four inches of rain in seven hours, and anemometers in the outlying districts recorded winds up to ninety miles an hour. Accounts of its wreckage filled columns in the newspapers for days. "A West Indian Hurricane Brings Ruin In Its Train," was a summary heading of the story on the morning of the 25th.

This storm occurred before the days of radio, and the area of its origin, its course of travel and its daily progress, slow in forward movement as with all hurricanes, was not known for weeks, until various long-voyage vessels arrived and sent in their observations. It was then known that the storm had originated several hundred miles from the Cape Verde Islands off the west coast of Africa, an ocean region of hot and stagnant air known as the doldrums, where swirling disturbances form and move westward with the drift of the trade winds. The first observation of the cyclone swinging toward the New World was on August 15th from vessels between African and South American or West Indian ports. Other vessels, west of the Azores, reported the passage of the storm up to the 20th, when it was several hundred miles east of the Virgin Islands, and the traffic between the United States and South America brushed it. On the 21st it was north of Puerto Rico, thence it moved to south of Bermuda, changing its course from west to northwest. On the early morning of the 23rd it was just south of Hatteras and speeding in forward travel as hurricanes go, having covered about six hundred miles since the previous day. Late on the evening of the 23rd it struck New York. On the morning of the 25th it covered a storm area about two hundred miles in diameter at the mouth of the St. Lawrence, whence it recurved southeastward, taking seven days to reach the Azores, which it passed and on September 2nd was north of the Madeiras; but its identity is fairly well established with a storm which lashed the coast of Spain two days later, after which it moved into a hot, dry area and expired.

Tingling from that night of August 23rd and the early morning of the 24th, I went tense again in reading on the 29th that another hurricane had devastated the coast of Georgia on the 28th and passed inland. It rushed westward past New York on the 30th and, instead of losing force in quitting contact with the sea, swung terrific winds from the east, southeast, then northwest. Again there was a rush of clouds that looked as if they had been shot from cannon, and an overwhelming storm tide. Waves and spray shot over Battery Park a full two hundred feet. The newspapers described Liberty as a statue rising from the waters, with no visible island base. What a week for a weather observer!

I have never quite recovered from that orgy of storm grandeur. My reaction was then, of course, not so analytical as it would be now, with radio advice and a set of weather instruments. Again and again as the years have gone by, I have watched for a repetition when mature deductions might be made, but the events of 1893 in New York may never be repeated in a natural lifetime. So I have journeyed to the tropics to meet these storms, but ships have dodged them, and ashore I have either been too early or too late. I have carried my recording instruments wherever I have gone. I remember one bitter disappointment. It was in September of 1928 while I was visiting my good friend James H. Scarr, chief of the U. S. Weather Bureau, atop the Whitehall Building in New York, that the series of incidents started. At Mr. Scarr's request I had brought some barograms and thermograms recorded in Costa Rica.

"You might pack up your barograph and start down to southern Florida," he suggested with a smile. "You like excitement."

"Do you think that hurricane in the Atlantic is going to strike Florida?" I asked, for I had heard advisory warnings about a cyclone which was moving westerly from where it had formed somewhere between the West Indies and the west coast of Africa. Its progress was about three hundred miles a day, and it had been under observation about four days.

"Between you and me and the lamp post," was his answer, "I think it will. It looks as if air pressure would block a recurve to the northeast."

Here was advice from one of the keenest meteorologists in the government service.

I had gone to the Weather Bureau in a calm state of mind. I left it in a fluster of excitement and misgivings. Several grave elements of doubt were in my mind. One concerned a bank account drained by a recent trip to Costa Rica; another was the obstacle of cancelling my salary during the journey to and from Florida, for storm observations could not be rated as an official part of my Zoölogical Park job. I would get to work on my check book in the morning, figure on an advance of salary to date, and determine whether there would be enough left over to carry me to the next salary.

With railroad fares and auto hire standing in bold and cruel figures at the top of a page, I pretty well wore down the point of a pencil in scrambling together my resources. It wouldn't work out; I couldn't go.

The saddest thought was that I could reach Florida in plenty of time. The journey would not consume much over thirty-five hours and there would be ample time to hire a car and seek a favorable location. The storm was about four days' travel from the Florida coast, having just crashed Guadeloupe, in the West Indies. The only soothing thought was the possibility that this hurricane would, as many did, take an unexpected course and head for Mexico or go raging northward into mid-Atlantic.

But it didn't. On September 13th it roared over Puerto Rico during eight hours of what was recorded as one of the world's greatest storms, with the barometer incredibly low. On the 14th it was north of Haiti,

To any but the keen observer clouds may be deceptive. The great domes of cumulus in the upper scene ushered in a gentle shower, while the thin and streaky cirrus (*lower*) was the advance storm sheet of an intense cyclone.

Various islands of the West Indies have their characteristic life—found nowhere else. The giant forest chameleon lives only in Cuba, while the powerful rhinoceros iguana is a Haitian species.

on the 15th the Bahamas were in the swirl, and on Sunday, the 16th, in the late afternoon, the "superhet" in my laboratory was bringing in the radio voice of a Palm Beach announcer in Florida:

"The sky is saffron-green and ragged clouds are racing overhead. Wind squalls are changing to explosive gusts. . . . The bottom is dropping out of the barometer. A surf thirty feet high is thundering on the beach. The great swells are streaming with spindrift like drifting snow. . . . Palm trees have been uprooted and are rolling like barrels along the beach. . . ."

So there it was—with me anchored in New York. That was the famous Palm Beach hurricane, which dropped the glass to 27.40, then an all-time record for Florida. It took me a week to shake off the dull rankling which came from missing that storm, and I'm still a bit sullen about it.

During the summer of 1936, on a steamer bound for the West Indies, there were reports of a hurricane east of the Leeward Islands. I took it for granted that the captain would dodge it. It passed well east of us, throwing out a strong radial swell. We were too far away to notice manifestations in the sky, though the vessel rolled heavily.

Several days later our wireless brought reports that the storm was headed for New York. From thrilling radio broadcasts about what was going to happen, I figured that in these days of wireless, this was the most heralded storm New York had ever known. Remembering the thrilling night in Brooklyn, and imagining the possible repetition of one of the high spots in my youth, I wished ardently that I were back in New York.

That storm of September 18, 1936, in the New York area, however, although it aroused much excitement in anticipation, was not of much force, not so severe ashore as many winter northeasters. The intense area remained out at sea, then recurved to the northeastward. The lowest barometer at the Weather Bureau in New York City was 29.65, with the highest recorded wind at forty-eight miles an hour. There were about four inches of rain, but it was distributed over a period of twenty-two hours. When I heard that the inshore kick-up had not amounted to much, I continued the tropical journey with no qualms of disappointment.

I have gone into all this detail in the hope that it will start some young readers on studies that may prove as fascinating as mine have been to me. There is a big difference between knowing why things happen and merely realizing that they occur. To me, the weather is part of natural history. It puts on grand shows; it intrigues, puzzles and surprises.

Owen Oliver, a veteran member of the editorial department of the *New York Sun*, has advanced an interesting theory about March gales. It is his idea that these vigorous spring winds form one of Nature's methods of grooming the forests for the awakening soon to come, that the tossing of boughs activates the flow of sap and the rush of air strips away dead branches and old leaves. Mr. Oliver's theory is certainly worth consideration during the days when the wooden rake is assigned to action after its winter rest.

Chapter XI

THE WHYS OF A SNOWSTORM

It may seem inconsistent that a frequenter of the tropics should retain a love for winter. I have probably annoyed those around me, when the time came for inrushing cold, by revelling in it, anticipating storms, and in the midst of the worst of them expressing pleasure when others were condemning what they called vile conditions. And I have actually enjoyed driving an automobile through a foot of snow, backing up and battling my way through drifts, or arriving at my office with the car sheathed in ice. I am sorry when a storm is over and depressed when the weather is mild during the winter. All this happens when I am at home, moored to my job. Under such conditions winter comes on like another act in a play.

Once in a while I have had a chance to go off on a sort of winter rampage. I remember one that was practical, and thus excusable, for I had contracted with a university to deliver a lecture on the seasons. The motion picture reels on that subject which I used ordinarily showed chiefly the effect of the varying weather of the seasons on the habits of animals; hence the lecture was basically zoölogical. The committee at the university, however, suggested that I bring a reel dealing specifically with the weather, to step up the interest in a newly formed and experimental class in meteorology. I had advocated such studies. Here was an opportunity of their being put into practice.

I made the new reel intermittently within a total time of about forty-eight hours. I was interested chiefly in its showing how much can be done in analyzing the parts of a single storm and in its demonstrating how attractive such a subject can be to young people.

The lecture was to be in late February. I decided to analyze a snowstorm, from the first hints in the sky to its ending, and I expected to be able to film such a storm some time during January or early February. If it didn't come along, I could make up a weather reel from odds and ends in the film vault, but such a reel would contain a large number of animated diagrams and lack the interest of what I had in mind.

The combination of favorable conditions on the weather map began to appear during the third week in January. A high-pressure area, such as produces the cold waves of winter, was forming over Alaska. These high-pressure areas are down-pressing and radiate intensely cold air in the vicinity of their advance. I estimated that the approach and rate of travel of this formation would bring it close to New York in about four days.

The second feature of the weather map was the intensification of the relatively low pressure that lurks over the deserts of southern California and Arizona. Here is a breeding ground for some of the most severe winter storms that reach the East. The "Low" in the southwest which had extended into New Mexico indicated that it was starting easterly travel as a developing storm. Figuring from the averages of winter storm tracks, I expected it to cross Texas to the lower Mississippi Valley, Alabama, and Georgia, and then to swing up the coast. Around the "Lows" the winds flow inward, that is, this storm would sweep moisture from the Gulf of Mexico—a condition that puts the very devil into "Lows" having their origin over the deserts. At a normal rate of travel this storm would reach the eastern coast in about three days. If the weather movements were as predicted, the front of the Alaska "High" would come in contact with the "Low" encroaching on the New York district and produce the type of snowstorm which costs the metropolitan district close to a million dollars to clear away.

Several things could happen. The tracks of weather movements have shunts from the main line which are very disturbing to the forecaster by throwing his deductions awry. The Alaskan "High" might rush down the Great Plains and so not reach the East as a cold wave. In doing this it would push the southwestern storm into the Gulf of Mexico, whence it would carom into the Atlantic off Florida. Or the "High" might continue to build, and fail to move. In this case, with the Mississippi Valley open as an avenue, following a favorite practice of travelling up the great river, the "Low" would rush to the Great Lakes and from there follow the broad St. Lawrence out to the sea. That would mean a southerly wind in the Eastern States, with mild weather and rain. The only hope for snow from such a storm was to be on its western side, where the counter-clockwise winds were northeasterly and racing parallel with the winds of an approaching "High."

These two weather movements, however, were running ideally for a snowstorm on the eastern coast. The "High" advanced southeasterly, keeping the "Low" on a southern course. In the late afternoon of the day before the storm arrived in New York, the center was over Alabama. The sky would have been called "cloudless" by the casual observer, but at sunset a careful study of the southwestern horizon revealed faint streaks, like dust, the first outflung whisps of cirrus, a thousand miles in advance of the approaching "Low." Such streaks mean something in winter. The first recording of the storm was made from the roof-top, with telephoto lens and ray filter to intensify the faint cloud appearances.

The next morning came the official weather forecast: "Increasing cloudiness followed by snow, probably heavy, beginning late this afternoon or tonight. Increasing northeasterly winds."

The slaty gray sky, its streaking and dappling, the

dulling spot where the sun rode behind the thickening sheet, called for technique in photography. A high ceiling of cirrus became underrun with alto-stratus and paths of the dappled alto-cumulus. As the main body of the storm approached, the heavens assumed an indefinable softness, across which background soon appeared smoky, rapidly moving veils. These ushered in the area of precipitation. The fast-moving clouds are known as nimbus. They move in the opposite direction from the clouds of the high ceiling or storm-sheet, in fact they appear to move into it. They are a part of the swirl of the cyclonic formation and while, to the observer, they seem to be following a straight course, they are actually a part of the counter-clockwise wind that is swirling around the disturbance.

The cloud changes of that morning and early afternoon were recorded on the film. By mid-afternoon the first light flakes were falling, and from that point the development was rapid. Soon the distant landscape looked foggy from the thickening fall. It was then that I took my last scenes of the day, one of the woods beginning to look frosted with an accumulation of a quarter of an inch of snow, and another to show the falling flakes against a slope of dark pines. The latter scene was interesting in that it showed the character of precipitation from overlapping banks of nimbus at different elevations. Through a fall of flakes of moderate size came larger ones, at first quite widely spaced. Then gradually the larger flakes dominated, slowly giving way again to smaller ones as the upper winds merged the strata of the clouds.

The reader may wonder how it is possible to take pictures of a snowstorm under overcast skies, when photography is supposed to be carried on in sunshine. The development of the motion picture film has rendered such photography readily possible, even under most unfavorable light conditions. One thing I discovered, however, in experimenting with scenes of falling snow, was to attach a shielding funnel, extending from the lens of the camera, which looked like a megaphone and was about four feet long. Without it, descending snow flakes close to the lens look like white streaks and blur the scene.

That night I worked in the studio. The fires were allowed to go out, the windows were opened, and when the place was well below freezing, a table was set underneath a roof-trap operated by a pulley, which enabled me to open and close it quickly. With the camera focused on a black velvet panel and an enlarging lens applied, I was ready to start.

A sparkling shower, like particles of mica, drifted downward past the quartz lights.

Snowflake photography, I should like to say in passing, is fascinating work. During the approach of a storm, and sometimes during its recession, the crystals are of marvelous designs. A close look at one's coat sleeve will demonstrate this, but highly magnified snowflakes are like exquisite jewels. The definable ones are always six-sided. They may be flat and plain, like cut crystal, or they may have radial designs like the circular arrangement of palm or fern leaves, but always there are six points. Not long ago an amateur photographer sent in some photographs of snow flakes that were triangles and insisted that the six-sided theory was all wrong, since here were three-sided snow crystals. He was shown that the "points" of the triangles were blunt or minutely squared off, and that the examiner with a magnifying glass was able to count two angulations at each end of the triangle—which proved, therefore, the existence of six points. Also, while the triangular crystals appeared similar at first sight, yet upon closer examination one found inner, striated markings and concentric lines, which differed markedly, no two being alike.

With a storm of great intensity, the precipitation may change to extremely small, hair-like particles which whirl like dust but, when microscopically examined, are seen to be six-sided rods. Still another form, with blizzard-like conditions, is like minute millet seeds, but being midway between snow and sleet, the particles are shapeless.

The snowflakes that night were of the crystal form, and the temptation was to panoram the lens from one section of the velvet to another, since snowflakes, like finger prints, are never exactly alike. It was this thought that kept me panoraming until I heard the end of the four-hundred-foot film roll flip into the take-up magazine. As the movie photographer is always seeking effects and continuity, I reloaded, went out on the side road and tried an experimental scene of the snow streaming past an electric light. It turned out to be a beautiful shot.

The following morning the snowstorm was in full blast. On flat portions of the roof there was a depth of a foot, the top margins projecting like shelving ledges, the edges streaming with drift. So thick was the fall, which descended in streams driven by the wind, that all the landscape except near-by objects was blotted out.

In thus watching the density of precipitation, one notices the fogging of distant objects, a phenomenon that may be noted in snow storms if one has lived in the same place for a number of winters, and been observant. Let the scene be a distant hill, a nearer hill, a church steeple a quarter of a mile away, and some trees midway between the steeple and the observer. While close around the observer, the snow may seem to be falling fast, the actual density of the fall and the rate of its accumulating depth upon the ground are best judged by its density in blocking out distant objects. If the distant hill has faded from sight but the one midway shows as a dim silhouette, the fall is light, probably not much over a quarter of an inch an hour. The fogging out of the nearer hill means, of course, a heavier fall, and if the church steeple disappears the fall may be an inch an hour, which is very heavy snow. If the midway trees disappear in a haze, the fall may be as much as an inch and a half an hour, which is exceptional but sometimes occurs in our eastern storms.

By noon the storm had changed its character. Distant objects appeared, but the amount of precipitation had not lessened. There had been a transformation in the flakes, which had become smaller until finally sleet sounded like coarse sand driven against the observatory windows. The red line on the thermograph was rising —and the barometer was falling sharply. This meant that the center was coming abreast of New York, off the coast. Very shortly afterward, the sleet was mixed with rain.

Such a change, during a coastal snowstorm, comes from the violent winds near its center picking up warm ocean air. Close to that center, in the advance, the wind was dead east and hurling warmed nimbus clouds over the shore. If the storm passage was slow, there would be plenty of rain and a sloppy landscape. But this was not to happen.

The barometer continued its descent, showing an increase in intensity and rapid movement. The wind shifted to the north as the storm moved on, and the rain changed back to snow of a powdery kind that raced like the dust of a prairie storm in a howling gale now fed in by the encroaching "High" that had arrived from Alaska.

This kept up well through the night, with blizzard conditions and mounting drifts. Lucky it was for the eastern cities that the period of rain, as the center passed, had packed the major fall of that snow, for if it had been added to the drifts of the later fall, the countryside would have been well tied up.

There was a curious manifestation that night which I have seen in howling snowstorms after dark. It occurs across the fields where eddies of snow are picked up and whirled along, and I can account for it only as a kind of static electricity. There are bluish flashes of light, instantaneous and appearing to be in the air, not far above the ground. They are quicker than a lightning flash, but I have had it demonstrated that some are bright enough to show shadows from weed stalks protruding from the snow.

The sun rose on an almost cloudless sky, a few tufts of white moving across the blue. The barograph pen had shot upward, the thermograph downward. The temperature was ten degrees and with just enough breeze to fill the air lightly with particles that glittered like diamond-dust. I had the job ahead—in high boots, short coat and mittens—of lugging the camera for the final shots of drifts, snow craters at the bases of trees, and the always attractive winter scenes of shadows across unbroken snow.

The description of that storm may seem clear enough, but how about making a movie of it; what had been accomplished; what was the "script" in arranging the scenes?

Four four-hundred-foot reels had been filmed. They went to the laboratory for development and the negative was returned and examined. All the scenes had been successfully exposed. There were sixteen hundred feet of film to be cut down to nine hundred feet, the best length for a standard reel, with running time of about ten minutes. With the story of the storm outlined (but not the detailed activities of the photographer), a list of the scenes, as they were cut and spliced, is as clear as a script in presenting such a reel. They show what it is possible to do in recording a storm by means of photography. Moreover, they demonstrate how much may be observed about a storm. The continuity of the film scenes follows:

Scenes:

1. Weather map three days before the storm.
2. Animated tracks of Alaska "High" and storm "Low."
3. Sunset; faint cirrus streaks in southwest.
4. Sunset; wind vane pointing westerly (fadeout).
5. Fade into gray morning sky; streaky cirrus haze.
6. Under-running alto-stratus clouds; dull sun spot.
7. Under-running alto-cumulus clouds from southwest.
8. Wind vane verring past N toward NE.
9. Fragments of nimbus clouds coming out of NE.
10. Wind vane swinging from NE.
11. First flakes of precipitation (against dark background).
12. Mixture of large and small flakes descending.
13. The ground whitens (fadeout).
14. Night—snow falling past street light (fade).
15. Close-magnified snow flakes—a number of them.
16. Close-magnified snow flakes—selecting star formation.

17. Close-magnified snow flakes—selecting pattern formation.
18. Close-magnified snow flakes—selecting flower-like formation.
19. Morning—heavy snow on roof.
20. Edge of roof—drifting snow streaming off.
21. Long shot, showing dim, distant objects.
22. Against dark background; changing character of precipitation.
23. Close-magnified sleet on velvet panel.
24. Instruments; descending barograph; rising thermograph.
25. Far shot; clear view of distant objects through sleet.
26. Rain against window pane.
27. Wind vane veering toward North.
28. Against dark background; precipitation changing back to snow.
29. Fine, wind-driven snow in clouds (fadeout).
30. Night effect—snow like smoke driven past street light.
31. Rapidly ascending line of barograph (fade).
32. Morning; sun casting shadows from trees.
33. Wind vane swinging from West with background tufts of clouds.
34. Snow craters from wind at base of trees.
35. Big drift curled over at top.
36. Measuring depth of snow.
37. Struggling snow plow opening side road.

There were no titles. The reel was explained verbally. When it was projected on the big screen of the university I felt a curious reaction, a combination of exhilaration and triumph. This was not self-commendation for the success of a technical job. Rather it had to do with something many years in the past, when I had timidly approached the lecturer on the weather, at the Museum of Natural History; when the wind vane I watched was not a big double-tailed "official" type with electric commutator, but a gilded horse atop a livery stable.

Chapter XII

CHAIN OF ISLANDS

My first trip to the West Indies was made about three years ago. Cuba and Jamaica were familiar to me, but the chain beginning with the Virgin Islands, then sweeping far southward to Trinidad, was new. These islands were a lure. I returned to them in 1935 and again in the summer of 1936.

To appreciate fully the curious distribution of animal life in the West Indies, the reader should have a fair-sized map to turn to occasionally from the text. The animal life keeps changing along the chain of islands, which is very surprising considering the comparatively small size of the greater number of them. In the big sweep from Cuba to Grenada, the animal life may be properly called West Indian; at Tobago it abruptly changes to South American. Without the complication of geological terms, the parade of islands has seemed to me to fall into several classifications. Cuba, Jamaica, Hispaniola, Puerto Rico and the Virgin Islands have their placid mountains with no signs of volcanoes. Immediately south of the Virgin Islands, which have no tropical forests, the close-knit islands of the Leeward and Windward chain (that is, those in crescentic alignment) are volcanic. Nearly every island has the unmistakable profile of an extinct volcano. Some of the smaller islands look like little more than an old volcano rising from the sea. Several, among them Montserrat, St. Lucia, St. Vincent and Martinique, have live volcanoes —of majestic proportions on the two last mentioned, their craters having broken forth in recent years in some of the greatest eruptions in history. An eruption on St. Vincent in 1812 has been described, in a review of volcanic disturbances of the West Indies, in a publication of the National Geographic Society, as "one of the most appalling and destructive the world has ever seen. . . . The explosion was a most fatal and far-reaching cataclysm, being equalled in recent years only by that of Krakatoa in the Straits of Sunda." This volcano erupted again in 1902. Close to the east of these volcanic islands are Barbados and lesser islands which are similar to the Bermudas in that they are of coral formation.

Whether or not there was a "land-bridge" connecting Cuba and the adjacent large islands with the Central American mainland, and whether the volcanic islands to the southeast extended as a ridge from Trinidad and Tobago (the latter without doubt once part of South America) is a problem. The distribution of animal life knocks down various theories like a row of dominoes.

The Greater Antilles have various species related to the mainland forms and some which are entirely distinct. There are large boas and crocodiles, but no poisonous snakes, in spite of their being within a geological stone's throw of an infested mainland.

What explains Cuba and Hispaniola having the solenodon, a silly-looking mammal the size of a rabbit, with a soft and elongated snout protruding from jaws with long and powerful teeth—a mammal with eyes not much larger than the head of a pin? Here is a form, which, according to fossil remnants from deeply imbedded rocks, was the first try-out in the age of dinosaurs toward four-legged, warm-blooded forms. It was not a success and its races gave way to better developed types. Yet this hangover survived through millions of years in the Greater Antilles. The only similar and related forms surviving from a dim past are to be found on the island of Madagascar. What an inconsistency in the theory of ancient land-bridges! What happened to related forms on the mainland? Why are Cuba and Hispaniola the last refuge for these remnants of the past?

The Bahamas, Cuba, Jamaica and Hispaniola have their indigenous iguanas—big lizards, with a body bulk like that of a terrier dog. What explains the separate species on close-lying islands? The same thing occurs with smaller lizards, all through the chain of islands. With the snakes the situation is as sharply defined. Large and important species of the boa family are scattered among the islands, distinct in species in different islands and distinct from mainland forms. This points to separation of the islands through a long period of geologic time, and the changing of related forms, owing to the necessity for change in habits and because of different terrain and food, to separate species. All this variation opens a vast field for the scientific observer in a study of the West Indies.

Aside from the animal life, an exciting prospect to me was a visit to Mount Pelee, a volcano even more dramatic than Vesuvius. As recently as 1902, after weeks of thunderous and sky-filling manifestations, it caused one of the tragedies most disastrous to human life in the history of the world—the annihilation of all of the inhabitants of a tropical city of 30,000 souls in a few moments' time.

On my first trip down the chain of islands an entomologist was aboard the vessel. His studies related chiefly to ants, of which the West Indies has more than enough. It was fascinating to leave the green background of an island, then see it turn blue with haze, and, after a couple of hours, to observe another rising from the sea—blue, then green, one after another, like "fade-ins" of a motion picture.

My friend, who was after ants and small anolid lizards or "chameleons," took lively advantage of the few hours ashore at each island. We hurried up the slopes to the wilder spots on each island, sometimes cutting through the backyards of little settlements, and stumbling over sleeping pigs, or being chased by lean dogs. The contingent of native youths which often followed us was not of much assistance. They poked their inquisitive black noses in our way when we were digging for ants, and were of little help in gathering lizards, although I offered the sum of three-pence a specimen on the British islands. The pretty little green or varicolored anolids ducked around tree trunks evading our snatching grasp. I considered that the act of closing the hand consumed a split second which gave them a chance to escape, and that a straight slap saved that fraction of a second and held the lizard imprisoned under one's hand. We adopted that method and so obtained species from all of the islands. There are over eighty kinds of these pretty changeable lizards, maintaining their numbers against the imported and omnivorous mongoose, due to the fact that the lizards are mostly arboreal.

At Antigua I saw unique evidences of combatting trouble from the over-bred and pestiferous mongoose, which had killed ground-prowling lizards, useful rodent-eating snakes and ground-nesting birds. In the parks and botanical garden of the little port, the stately palms have sheet-iron rat-guards around their trunks to keep rodents from invading and nesting among their fronds—since the rats even climb trees to evade the mongoose, which frightens them, but is not of much economic value as a ratter.

At Montserrat, which was rumbling with earthquakes, our investigation took us to a small crater among the hills which would have furnished fair inspiration for a description of Dante's *Inferno.* Boiling water seethed from crevices of rocks, ledges of sulphur surrounded the place and a sulphurous vapor saturated the air. I afterward found that all the silver coins in my pocket had turned black.

"What on earth is that shack doing up above this hell hole?" I asked Dr. Weber.

He said that it was an observation post for the volcanic observer from Martinique, Professor Perret, Curator of the Volcanic Museum at St. Pierre, and that the scientist was then in the States recovering from poisoning from volcanic fumes while he was making observations. He also told me that there were rumors that Montserrat might be the next blow-up in the West Indies, although Professor Perret thought that the volcanic gases, with their emission of steam, served as safety valves in protecting the island. That night the brass on our ship turned black. Later I heard that the crater on St. Vincent indicated the next show, since recording instruments on the mountains showed rising temperatures.

Guadeloupe (French) and Dominica (British)—luxuriant in tropical vegetation—were next on the southward voyage. Dominica had an extensive crater of steaming mud flats and boiling water, with sulphur-incrusted edges, which emitted growls, murmurs and hisses, proclaiming the cracked shell of a volcanic boiler beneath.

I rowed out to the steamer from Dominica feeling a mixture of surprise and amusement. Approaching that island I had thought of a letter in one of my satchels. It was from a scientist in Washington and read, in part:

"I hope you will have time to have a good visit in Dominica and I am enclosing a letter of introduction to a planter among the hills.

"There is a very handsome frog living in the higher streams and I am anxious to have specimens for our collection. It is as large as the bull frog of the States, pale, bronzy color, with big luminous eyes. You probably know it as *Leptodactylus fallax*. Animal dealers have offered me specimens at five dollars apiece, but I cannot afford to buy a series at such a price. If you stay over, you will no doubt be able to pick up some of them."

The steamer stop at Dominica was about four hours. There was no chance to visit the plantation in the mountainous part of the island. Wandering around the little town, with the vessel in sight at her anchorage, I came to the market place. All sorts of things from green to dried vegetables, strange-looking fruits and skinny, gasping fowls were in rows, with their black vendors gesticulating and chanting behind them. I stopped to glance at some varicolored, mongrel chickens. An aged colored woman near by beckoned energetically.

"Mountain chickens, mister, much finer and fresher, sir." She pointed to a round flat basket.

I strolled toward her, to stop her noisy soliciting. She cautiously tilted the cover of her basket. There was a mass of *Leptodactylus fallax,* fully a dozen, their backs gleaming like radiator bronze!

"How much?" I shrugged—the usual opening.

"A shilling each, very cheap, very fat."

Not to disappoint her in the expected dickering, though I was anxious to make a dive for that basket, I argued to the extent of making it my property for ten shillings and departed with it after it had been tied with ravelling from a grimy rope.

That was my prize from Dominica. Counting the big frogs on the ship, I found there were fourteen, and the total cost for the collection had been two dollars and a half, or just half the price of a single specimen quoted to my friend.

On Martinique the background of volcanic atmosphere is more sinister, but one must go to the northern side of the island to see it. Here the great mass of Mount Pelee rises to the clouds, its slopes sterile with strata of volcanic dust and mud, deeply furrowed by erosion from the rains. Fumes trail from the summit, and high up on the sides are crevices from which come steam and yellow vapors. At what seems to the eye quite a distance from its base lie the ruins of St. Pierre, half buried under volcanic precipitate in the great eruption of 1902, during which the entire population of over 30,000 people was wiped out in a few moments and the crews of ships at anchorage in the roadstead were also annihilated. The ruins of this city, destroyed in modern times, and the astonishing collection at the Volcanic Museum, where Curator Perret presides, have been like a magnet to me. The Curator is the official observer of the West Indies volcanic chain and I understand that he had recently constructed a tunnel into a slope of Mount Pelee and there installed microphonic instruments with wires leading to his headquarters. In this way he keeps the pulse of the giant under his observation.

On Martinique and the near-by Island of St. Lucia a new point of interest appeared in the presence of the fer-de-lance, the first instance of poisonous serpents all the way down the procession of islands. Whether this dangerous snake was introduced or not has been a subject for debate. Certain it is that the species does not occur on St. Vincent or Grenada to the southward. It inhabits Tobago and Trinidad, but those islands were connected in comparatively recent times with the South American mainland, where the fer-de-lance is a common and widespread species.

In recent years there have been assertions that the fer-de-lance was becoming "steadily scarcer" on both Martinique and St. Lucia, and in one publication I had found it spoken of as "almost exterminated on both islands." I was interested to check this and found that both assertions were incorrect. Possibly they were based on the establishment of the imported mongoose, now rated everywhere in the West Indies as a pest. True enough, the mongoose is common, but it does not inhabit the humid forest areas preferred by the fer-de-lance.

As one winds a tortuous way through the magnificent forests of Martinique, pendant with lianas, with horizontal branches thick with orchids, or through great bowers of tree ferns, the air is heavy with moisture, and scarcely an hour passes without a fall of warm rain. Here is the home of the fer-de-lance, where contours run up and down in steamy canyons or rise to peaks four and five thousand feet high. In such areas the mongoose is seldom seen. It prefers drier, flatter ground. I talked to a number of people in Martinique and the fer-de-lance was declared not infrequent, but it lives in thick places, where little planting is done. Again, on St. Lucia a canyon was described where the mountain streams had brought down masses of rounded boulders, and here the fer-de-lance was "common enough" and bounties were annually paid for specimens without appreciably diminishing its numbers.

I think the mongoose is afraid of the fer-de-lance. In its native India it attacks the cobra without hesitation, but the cobra strikes slowly, in a sweeping bow. There is a big difference between the sweep of a cobra and the lightning-like dart of the fer-de-lance, whose fangs are of such length that they can pierce to the vitals of the mongoose. Even in Martinique and St. Lucia, with their poisonous snakes, respect for the mongoose is nil, except for the bounty offered for it on islands where there is no pretense of making use of it, but only bitterness against its depredations among poultry and wild birds.

Bounties run as high as six-pence for male specimens and double that amount for females, or in the latter case, the equivalent of approximately a quarter of a dollar in United States money. On islands where the bounties were highest, a smuggling trade developed from other islands—specimens being brought in packed in ice. The authorities were disturbed by the inexhaustible supply of mongoose, but continued to pay bounties until the smugglers started a specific bootleg game. By delicate surgical work, freshly dead male specimens of mongoose were made to appear like females. The deception was skillfully done, but the preponderance of females was suspicious, and investigations disclosed and shattered a profitable trade. Bounties among the islands have now been largely dispensed with. The South American, Central American and United States governments are rigid in their restrictions against specimens of the mongoose being admitted to any of the ports, even for exhibition in zoölogical gardens.

There are hopeful signs that the mongoose in the West Indies is deteriorating, as is usually the case with forms of life that breed out of bounds. I have seen specimens running across roads and trails that were inferior in size and pelage to what the mongoose should be. The tail should be brushy, and I have seen examples with the tail almost bare, like that of a rat. Also, it has been found that the larger harmless snakes are learning to attack and eat the mongoose. Two were found in a boa that had been run over by a planter's auto. A litter of young mongoose was found in a smaller boa, showing that the snake had prowled into the carnivorous animal's nest. Despite the fear of all snakes among West Indian negroes, the harmless kinds are now grudgingly being admitted to be of some use.

Leaving Grenada, with Trinidad—my destination—a day ahead, we discarded our khaki clothes, sweaty from a shore collecting trip, floated in the pool and met in the smoking room for a conversational review of the islands. The entomologist's work had been very successful. He had gathered a fine series of ants, and a great variety of minute insect forms which he was studying, each batch separately preserved and tagged with its island locality. Obtaining the small insect forms was possible under a new technique which yielded far better results than former methods.

The collecting part of this work consisted in gathering leafy branches and débris from the forest floor and packing them in tight canvas bags. Arriving on shipboard, the débris was placed in a sheet-metal receptacle which looked like an oven. The bottom sloped downward in a funnel-like form, its lower portion resting in a jar of alcohol. An electric lamp in the receptacle started things going. It heated and dried the air in the oven; there was a grand exodus of insect forms from the débris, all sliding to a resting place in the alcohol jar. The variety of species forming a stratum in the jar was surprising. There was little hint of it when the material was being collected.

"It certainly gives results on these short island stops," said Dr. Weber. "I had a whole night's work down here last year go wrong under curious circumstances. I was studying the nocturnal flying forms, and went out equipped with a sheet and flashlamp, the idea being to hang up the sheet and shine the light on it for a few minutes. Moths and flying beetles would come fluttering toward the sheet. I was searching for moths and it required considerable dexterity to get them. After some waiting, I was wielding a small net when an insectivorous bat swooped in front of me and grabbed the prize. Considering this an incident only, I waited for another arrival and was checkmated again by my aerial rival. So taking down my apparatus I went to another spot, but the bat followed me, and I had to give it up."

Later, in the smoking room, some business men came to a near-by table and started a loud and interminable discussion about the problems concerned with the selling of women's apparel. It seemed to me that they were getting nowhere; that these same things must have been discussed many times before, and I wondered why their emphatic suggestions had not been put into effect—if they were any good. At any rate, it was their right to talk about anything they pleased; I was interested to see how men's minds run in different channels.

As I stood a moment later on deck where the only sound was the bow wash, volcanoes were uppermost in my mind. The slopes of Mount Pelee, with whisps of vapors from its crevices, remained like a picture in the ship's wake. When I was a boy I selected books in which volcanoes formed the high spots—the adventure books of Collingwood and Ballantyne. Later I accumulated formal books about eruptions and longed to see some of the world's fiery mountains in action. Why did these outbursts from the earth occur? There were those lava needles collected near Vesuvius, incandescent rods hurled to the heavens, pairs of them fusing in the form of perfect crosses. What tremendous heat caused this! There were those tubes with layers of ejected and precipitated dust from eruption, given me by the volcanic observer. The mountain had ejected blue, yellow, red, gray, white, and dark brown clouds of talc-fine dust, then mud and molten lava. What had been going on, deep down below? The finer brown dust-clouds, he had said, had been hurled ten miles high and had formed a ceiling of ruddy, insulating dust around the world, filtering the sun and thus producing an exceptionally cold winter. I had seen Vesuvius, Stromboli, and Aetna, but only when they were merely staining the sky with trailing vapor. Then there was Mount Lassen, in California. I was able to go west the year after its eruption in 1914, but Lassen was slumbering again. A few years after that, Irazu had erupted in Costa Rica, and on hearing rumors of renewed activity, I had gone there, but nothing had happened.

Here was a scientist on a zoölogical quest dreaming of volcanoes. I was snapped out of it by the clanking of winches on the loading deck. They were getting ready for Trinidad and that meant I would soon be going ashore, bag and baggage. It was high time to think about packing, and my letters of introduction to set me on my way.

It was soon evident that Trinidad would offer new and particularly favorable kinds of collecting experiences. This was because of the narrow but good roads which wound over the mountains, through virgin tropical forest, bamboo jungles that towered as high as trees, and miles of palm groves. One could stop a car at any number of likely-looking places, prowl around until satisfied, and then drive on to another place.

There is a drawback in working at night. Swarms of flying staphalynid beetles, not much over an eighth of an inch in length, fill the air in unexpected places. This beetle has a way of getting into one's eyes, and when blinked under the lid, it ejects an acid. There is an instantaneous and almost unbearable pain which may last a quarter of an hour.

I never visited an area where entomologists were so systematically aligned to carry on man's battle against the insect world. In the first few days of reconnoiter, Dr. E. J. Sankeralli, of the Malaria Laboratory, showed me the method of combating mosquitoes in salt marshes of the island. The malaria mosquitoes are fond of a certain salinity, but cannot endure too high a content in the breeding places of their aquatic larvae. An ingenious type of rapid, ditch-digging machine has been devised, and with this equipment narrow ditches are extended to the level of low tide. With a rise of the tide the strongly saline water backs into the marshes and impregnates the ground with salt content that ruins such places as mosquito-breeding grounds. Other entomologists are working on the problem of fruit flies. I found also that the government was producing an anti-venomous serum for the stings of scorpions. While the scorpion, centipede, and big brown spider or tarantula are not true insects, the entomologists include them in their studies. Of the three, the scorpion is by far the most dangerous, although the least formidable in appearance. The Trinidad scorpion is a dull brown creature, not longer than a man's finger, and looks like a miniature lobster with a curved sting on its tail. A jab of that sting, however, may throw a man into convulsions and paralyze a limb for several days. Fatal cases have been recorded with adults of slight physique; and with children under fourteen, unless immediate remedial measures are used, there is a strong probability that the case will be fatal. Poultices of yellow laundry soap are considered helpful because the alkaline soap neutralizes the acid of the scorpion's barbed tail. The hideous-looking centipede, which in parts of Trinidad grows to be fourteen inches long and bites with canaliculated fangs, is considered dangerous, while the bite of the tarantula is but mildly so, because of the minute poison openings on its fangs. It seems strange that these great spiders should be rated as mildly poisonous, while the little "black widow" of the United States is highly dangerous. However, in recent studies of the latter, it has been estimated that its poison is about ten times more toxic than that of other spiders and that the ejection openings on its fangs are relatively larger.

In Trinidad, the mammal life is that of South America, the West Indian fauna being abruptly left behind on leaving Grenada. The only reminder is the destructive mongoose, which has thinned the birds and nearly exterminated the ground-running lizards. Of the native mammals there are two kinds of monkeys, the big brown howler and a capuchin. There are thirty-four kinds of bats, representing nine distinct families. Among them are the giant bat, the vampire and a large species which feeds upon fish and hides by day in caves which reek with fishy odors. There are the fruit squirrel, twelve species of mild mice, the agouti and the paca. Of the carnivores the leopard cat or ocelot is not uncommon, but the mainland jaguar does not occur. Other carnivores are the crab-eating raccoon, the tayra, and the tropical otter. The manatee or sea "cow" is common enough in the extensive Nariva Lagoon. The collared peccary and a small species of deer are the only wild, hoofed animals. The so-called toothless animals or edentates are represented by the tree ant-eater or tamandua, the little silky ant-eater and the armadillo. There are several kinds of opossums, large and small. One of the latter is not much bigger than a mouse, and feeds upon insects.

The reptile life is of South American kinds represented on the near-by mainland, but with omissions that seem curious when it is noticed that large and important varieties occur.

There is a common crocodilian—the rough-eyed cayman—of rather small size, inhabiting the Nariva Lagoon, which is also the home of big anacondas, or water boas. The boa constrictor, tree boa and rainbow boa are common. There are many attractive colubrine snakes, including the big and slender black and white rat snake, which looks like a Japanese creation in shining lacquer. The dangerous coral snake occurs in the forests, the fer-de-lance grows big, and the bushmaster is often reported in various parts of the island. Curiously enough, the mainland tropical rattlesnake has never been recorded.

Coming north from the first stay in Trinidad, we carried with us a good series of reptile specimens, chiefly snakes, in the forward hold of the vessel. All the boxes and crates were laid flat on the steel floor, one level down, so that in case of roll or pitch nothing could topple over and be broken. Moreover, slats were fastened to the boxes, so that they were in immovable blocks. The snake boxes were of warp-proof wood and screwed together. All the ventilation holes were covered with copper mesh to prevent the escape of young snakes, if they should be born—a precaution I had taken many times before. Every box had been carefully scrutinized before it went aboard the loading tenders and examined again when it came aboard the ship, to see if anything had happened to it during handling. The escape of any kind of snake, even a small, harmless species, is inexcusable on a passenger ship. A nervous passenger, with an idiosyncrasy against reptiles, might be thrown into a bad state of mind and the line be subjected to serious complaint.

Imagine then, my consternation when a steward rapped sharply at the door of my cabin and announced that something must have escaped, for quite a crowd was looking down the forward hatch.

Rushing forward with a sense that my recent meal had suddenly stopped digesting, I saw the crowd, sure enough. Fingers were pointing here and there. In an instant beads of perspiration broke forth on my face.

Without stopping to ask about the cause of the excitement, I swung onto the narrow steel ladder leading to the lower level and found half a dozen of the crew dashing from one spot to another—and they were after my specimens!

But my breath returned, although it was labored. It was the collection of Dominican frogs that had caused the trouble. The boatswain, who daily brought down fresh water to be sprinkled on them, decided that they looked a bit dry and that he would perform the service himself. He poured some water on the frogs, then turned to fill another dipper. One of the frogs, taking the open panel for a good place to stretch his legs, leaped high in the air. The boatswain declared that he had never seen a game of "follow the leader" played with more snap than by that crate of frogs. With the regularity of the ticking of a clock, a stream of frogs leaped into space, and each, upon touching the deck, executed a jump of at least ten feet. They jumped in all directions but we caught all but one, which was never found. A small ventilating port was open to the sea and I thought it probable that he had gone through it like a circus performer through a ring.

Chapter XIII

QUEST OF THE GIANT BAT

It is jarring to a scientist to concede an error in his formal writings. However, I had that experience two years ago, and it led to one of the most important quests I have made. It produced a new history for an animal little known, and it resulted in the capture of an important species never before seen in a zoölogical garden.

It all started at the close of my 1934 stay on the island of Trinidad when Professor F. W. Urich, the government entomologist and an internationally known naturalist, called my attention to a passage in an article of mine about the vampire bat which related to a giant bat that carried the scientific name of *Vampyrus spectrum.* My reason for including mention of it in the vampire paper was to explain that it was thought by early naturalists to be *the* blood-sucking bat, while the much smaller and actual vampire had as yet not been scientifically named. Early naturalists dispatched by Linnaeus to the American tropics evidently got a great kick from tales told by the natives about bats that drank human blood, and when a creature with a wingspread of a yard was felled by a charge from a cannon-like shotgun of those days, its size and array of teeth fitted in well with the tales of sanguineous bats. Studying memoranda brought back by the early explorers, together with leathery remnants, Linnaeus also was impressed. The passage in my article to which Professor Urich took exception read:

> "The great naturalist Linnaeus, in 1766, gave this big but harmless bat the scientific name of *Vampyrus spectrum*, and owing to the rules of scientific precedence in the placing of a name, it will remain thus libeled."

"What do you mean by 'big but harmless bat'?" asked the professor.

"Why, that *Vampyrus* is conceded, in the few reliable descriptions I have found, to be a harmless fruit eater. How about Bates's notes during his observations in the Amazon Valley . . .?"

"I'm afraid he confused it with *Phyllostoma*—the big spear-nosed bat. *Phyllostoma* is a fruit eater."

"But *Vampyrus* is also a spear-nosed bat."

"Yes, but it far outranks *Phyllostoma* in size."

Then the professor told me this strange story:

"A few months ago a boy living in the interior of the island on a cocoa plantation was prowling around after dark. A cocoa plantation is like a jungle. There are shading, interlacing trees overhead and, in the steamy heat, these sheltering trees serve as hosts for parasitic air plants and orchids. Aerial vines become established from seeds carried by birds. Their resulting growth produces pendant roots or lianas. To the uninitiated, a stroll through cocoa planting might seem like an adventure in the wilderness. To the seasoned explorer, such areas provide good going; the cutting knife rests in the scabbard. The thick débris of the forest floor provides fascinating investigation for certain specialists such as the economic entomologist and the ant specialist. All kinds of the larger wild creatures prowl through cocoa plantations. Four bushmasters were killed in one such area.

"The boy who lived at the border of the plantation was keen on prowling and watching for wild life. He was wandering about with a flashlight not far from the house, watching for the awakening of life that takes place soon after dark. There were rustles among the fallen leaves. These, he deduced, must be made by fruit opossums, creatures which have a body about the size of a rat's. He wanted to catch one, since they are quickly tamed and make intelligent pets. Locating one rustle he followed it up. He came close to a small creature with lustrous gray hair, which was scratching the leaves aside and turned to look backward toward the beam of light with eyes that bulged and glowed. These temperamental creatures will bite with strong teeth when they are first restrained, so the boy was cautious. His idea was to wait until the opossum moved forward, then reach down and grasp it by the neck, or by the end of its long and prehensile tail.

"When the opossum was through for the moment with its scratching and nosing, it moved forward. Now was the moment to step forward and grasp it, but with the first step something happened. There was a swish of air from a beat of wings and an object the size of a hawk enveloped the opossum. The astonished boy was able to distinguish the form of a huge bat. Its teeth flashed as it grasped the opossum behind the head. There was a crunching of bone and the opossum collapsed. Then the bat took to the air, carrying the animal with it. There was no disputing the boy's story. He was not the type to exaggerate and build wild tales. A giant bat had flown off with a fruit opossum and no known bat of such strength existed on the island except *Vampyrus*."

"It sounds pretty wild," I said.

"Listen," was his emphatic rejoinder, "my assistant and I investigated the hollow trees of that area. *Vampyrus* does not live in caves with ordinary bats. We captured two in the hollow shaft of a silk-cotton tree . . ."

"You had two live specimens of *Vampyrus!*" I exclaimed.

"Yes, for a couple of weeks. They were restless devils. They had no interest in fruit, so I tried them with rats and a few birds Aschi shot for them. I was not prepared for their ravenous carnivorous appetites. They had a nasty fight one night and both were dead in the morning. And that is the animal you call a big but harmless bat!"

The fer-de-lance and the mongoose. The latter was not imported to the West Indies to kill the poisonous snakes, but to destroy rats. Among the islands the fer-de-lance occurs only on St. Lucia and Martinique, in densely tropical spots avoided by the mongoose. The latter is afraid of the reptile owing to the snake's speed in striking.

Giant silk-cotton tree with hollow shaft, within which at a height of about twenty feet was found a pair of giant bats.

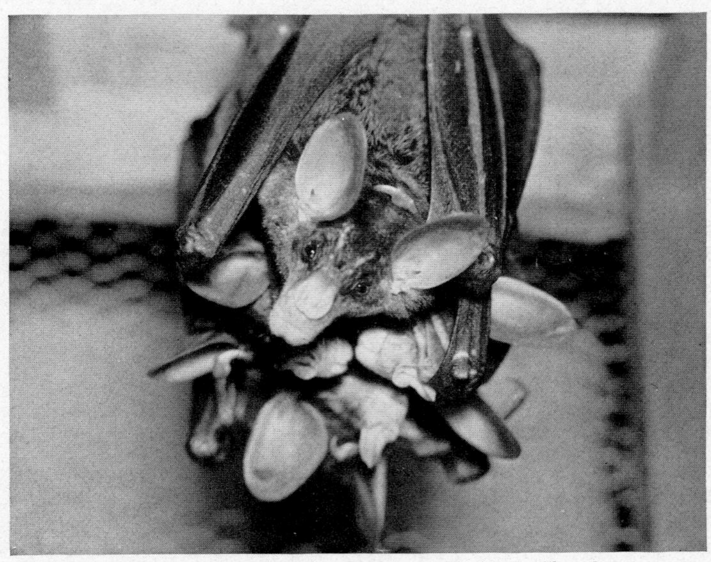

The two pairs of giant bats brought from Trinidad. They have a wing spread of a yard and are the first of their kind ever to be exhibited.

"It looks as if we'd have to revise the descriptions of *Vampyrus* in the natural history books. The species has never been exhibited. Do you think that if I concentrated on it this coming summer I could capture some and take them to New York?"

"I'll guarantee it," said the professor. "You and Aschi can search out silk-cotton trees and do plenty of crawling getting into the central, hollow chambers. That is where *Vampyrus* is to be found. The natives in several quarters report bats that look like big black kites. Those are the places in which to find your trees."

So it was decided that the summer of 1935 was to be allotted to the quest of *Vampyrus spectrum*.

Aschi drove around to my boarding place several days after I arrived in Port-of-Spain. The mapping of big silk-cotton or ceiba trees had not really started, for my arrival in Trinidad was followed by visits among the scientists. He came up to my room where I was dressing to go to dinner at the country club. In the tropical heat and moisture I was having trouble getting on a pair of silk socks. In the north they would have pulled on easily. Now they had to be worked on like a new pair of kid gloves.

"We start early in the morning," said Aschi.

"To locate big trees?"

"I have found one," he said. "I crawled in with a flashlight. There is a pair of big bats."

Here was news, right at the beginning. Aschi said

that he would bring his car, a big net to cover holes around the base of the tree and a mesh cage we had made. Then he asked if I would ride with him.

When I remembered that Aschi's car was a Morris, with wheels not much larger than those of a bicycle, and that the net he spoke about made a pile like a hay-mound, I thought it would be well for me to travel in another car which I had commissioned for my stay. Besides, there were my camera and tripod and the water canteens.

A remarkable point about the island of Trinidad is its narrow but very smooth roads, which are made possible by the island's inexhaustible supply of asphalt from the great pitch lake. That was why we were able to use autos in going after the giant bats. I have been in no other tropical country where such a procedure would be possible, with the exception of Panama, with its American-built road to Madden Dam.

Still struggling with my socks I told Aschi that I would be ready and waiting at a specified time the next morning. When he had gone and dressing became less of a battle, I concluded that we might have a fair hike through the bush; but since Aschi had located the tree so quickly, it could not be very far from one of the island's trails. However, on second thought, since he could go through thick places like a weasel and was skillful with his cutting knife, it was problematical how far away it was. I hoped that the tropic forest, with its red soil, would not be too dense to obtain clear photographs. Scenes of the habitat of *Vampyrus spectrum* would be of great value in a scientific paper. So far as I knew, no such pictures had ever been made.

I was up early to get ready for the hard day ahead. My outfit consisted of a light khaki shirt, open at the neck, khaki trousers and knee-high laced boots. The boots were pulled over thin woolen socks which I dusted lightly with sulphur. That type of apparel is just about impervious to ticks and red bugs. It was the outfit I had adopted after being with the engineers in Panama when they cut into jungle in making camp to build the Madden Dam.

I tucked two rolled snake bags under my belt, and also my tropical rain cape which rolls into a compact cylinder. Then I checked the camera magazines and waited for Aschi. He came about an hour late, which was disturbing when I thought of all that must be done. However, the little Morris oozed billows of net and jointed sticks. There was no doubt about his having everything that was necessary. I saw that a native boy was with him and was glad to have this additional carrier. Aschi looked at me in his usual imperturbable way. He scorned boots, no matter where he went, and often went barefooted. I believe that this fine boy is of Hindu strain, and I have noticed a near immunity of the dark-skinned races to the attacks of ticks and insect pests.

My commissioned car, of ancient vintage but with plenty of leg room, was ready and I took the bat cage aboard. We were off, with the Morris scooting around corners and leading us a lively chase. We cleared Port-of-Spain and ran through the long procession of little houses outside which are occupied chiefly by Hindus, where scenes along the road with turbaned forms and the pungent odors of wood fires for cooking make one think of India. This gives way to farming country and beyond lie the wilder parts. For a long way out of town there is little evidence of tropics—some palms here and there, a few big umbrella-like trees, nothing more, except the ascending temperature.

We were still in the region of fairly wide roads and had been driving little more than an hour when the Morris pulled to the side of a farm fence under the shade of a big tree, and Aschi got out. Thinking that something had happened to his car, I joined him.

"What's wrong?" I asked.

"Nothing, doctor, this is the place."

"We go in from here?"

"No, this is the tree."

I could feel myself growing somewhat embarrassed after my elaborate morning preparations. The feeling was intensified when a member of the negro constabulary came strolling up in a snow-white, starched uniform and piped helmet. He came from a police telephone booth a few yards down the road, which I hadn't noticed. We were soon joined by some shiny-eyed children; then two cows, followed by a flock of chickens, wandered onto the scene.

What a background for the capture of the first specimens of *Vampyrus spectrum* ever to leave their native climes to be exhibited in a zoölogical garden! It seemed incredible that two of the great bats should be hiding in that tree.

The tree itself was noble enough, well over a hundred feet high and ten feet in diameter. Like many of the ceibas, it had a triangular opening which indicated that it was hollow.

Once again the glamour vanished, for the opening was so generous that Aschi stepped right in as if through a narrow doorway, and I followed him. My headband lamp was in the car. I hadn't even thought of reaching for it, but Aschi pulled a flashlight from his hip pocket and shot the beam upward. The hollow shaft was about five feet in diameter and twenty-five feet high. There were ledges along its sides. Suspended from the very top was a pair of huge bats that looked like inverted opossums because of their pinkish faces and big ears. At one side was a youngish one. They gibbered at us and ground their teeth together with a chattering sound.

My companion decided that his jointed stick was too short to reach them, and that we must cut a sapling outside, but before we could use it the opening of the tree must be covered with the net.

As we came out to get the appliances and the bat cage, it seemed like walking from a thrilling dream into very sordid reality. The children had been joined by their parents and the chickens were under everybody's feet.

After making careful preparations and with the net attached we crawled under, carrying the cage and a pliable sapling which we had trimmed of everything but a tuft of leaves at the top. We thrust this upward at the bats. Then we noticed with apprehension that the smaller specimen had disappeared. There were hollows behind the ledgelike projections of the rotting shaft. If the adult pair steered for these places, it might be impossible to get them.

Without more ado, we stirred the pair up with the tip of the sapling and again, in the beams of our lights, the inside of that tree was like another world. Fortunately the monster bats came right down to us. Aschi grabbed one by the back of the neck and, screeching like a monkey, it enveloped his shoulders with its leathery wings. Finally we worked it into the cage. By that time the second bat was clinging within the level of our faces. We opened the cage door and thrust the opening over its head and it hooked itself inside to join its mate. They clung to the side in inverted position, alternately thrusting their wings about each other for protection, reminding me of human arms with drooping capes enveloping a companion in sympathy.

"How did you find them?" I asked Aschi.

"It was this way, doctor. I was looking in all the hollow trees I could find, and outside this one I saw a rat's tail." He swung his light to our feet. We were standing on a mass of reddish woodpulp. Scattered all over the place were feathers, among which I recognized the bright primaries of the tropical bluejay. He picked up a curled object.

"What—another rat's tail!"

"Yes, doctor, they eat plenty of rats, but never the tails. We will look into more trees tomorrow."

I was anxious to start right away, but my companion suggested that we should go to the swamps and shoot some small birds for our captives, enough to store in the professor's icebox for several days. Aschi remembered the appetites of the professor's original pair.

When we came out of the tree it was interesting to see the astonishment of our audience. Not one among those people had ever seen one of these big bats close to. I questioned the adults and the intelligent policeman carefully. They said that they had sometimes seen big bats flying, but that they had no idea they were like this. There were squeals and shouts when the bats showed their big teeth and murmurs of respect when they gnashed these teeth as they had inside the tree.

Aschi went for the camera. A cow was standing in front of the tree, smelling the net. I said that we would wait until we got to a more remote location before we started taking photographs showing the homes of *Vampyrus spectrum*. We went to the swamps and shot some birds for our captives which were installed in Professor Urich's laboratory. Soon they were crunching bones and shaking feathers around the place. This encouraged us as to their ultimately arriving safe in New York.

Before I left the professor's place, he motioned me to a leather chair on his screened writing porch and signaled to a servant to bring rum punches. In spite of the screening there was a goodly variety of insects dancing around his lamp and crawling over the papers. A night lizard, or gecko, leaped to the top of a closed inkwell and regarded us with goggle eyes which looked strange because of their elliptical pupils.

"That's Otto," said the professor. "He always shows up around this time. It's annoying when he runs over unblotted manuscript."

I looked at Otto intently. He had just chewed up a moth and the dust from its wings was floating like mica scales under the lamp.

"Your 'big but harmless bats'?" quietly asked the professor.

"All wrong, but we'll straighten it out, thanks to you," I told him. "We're off again in the morning for more trees."

A search among the big trees in the more remote areas revealed no traces of giant bats up to the time when I decided to make a trip to Mayaro. The day's journey to that wild and magnificent beach has always fascinated me. It is one of the most beautiful beaches in the world, with miles of leaning coconut palms and golden-green surf tinted by the outpouring of the Orinoco. A considerable part of the route is at the edge of the Nariva Lagoon, where the anaconda or water boa grows to a huge size. The thickest snake we ever had at the Park came from this labyrinth of waterways and swamps. "Big Annie," as we called her, was close to twenty feet long and two feet in diameter—olive green, with big, round black spots.

Leaving Aschi to prowl for more trees I made the Mayaro trip. It was on this journey that I heard from a government ferryman the first account I have considered authentic of a big snake attacking a human with the possible intention of swallowing its victim. The ferryman had the lonesome job of pulling a flat scow back and forth by hand along a cable, as he transported occasional cars that came his way. A man visiting him stripped off his outer garments and jumped off the runway for a swim. Fortunately his modesty prompted him to retain a single undergarment. There was a swirl from under a ledgy bank and through the muddy water the swimmer made out the undulations of a huge snake coming at him. An instant later there was a mighty tug at the back of his single piece of clothing. Between the effort of the anaconda to yank the victim into its coils and the struggles of the man to prevent it, the garment gave way, and with furiously floundering strokes the swimmer gained the bank.

Returning from Mayaro I was awakened very early. Aschi had found another bat tree, with more feathers and more rats' tails. This time I put my guide through a cross-examination as to the location of the tree. Was it far; did we go through thick places?

He said that it was not more than twenty miles away, and again not far from a farm; but that there were no chickens, no fences, and there would be a fine background for pictures. The jungle-forest ran right down to the tree, but it was good walking, no bush to cut in getting through.

I remembered the policeman in his starched whites and had no intention of appearing again in such company clad in the garb of a tropic explorer. However, as Aschi was not very definite about the location of the prospective tree, I put on slacks, sneakers and a white shirt, open at the throat. It was a sort of fifty-fifty outfit.

We rode for about an hour with the same two-car arrangement. At last we stopped at a West Indian negro's farm—the house with a thatched roof. The big net was hauled from the back of the Morris. I put the bat cage beside it, then brought out my camera. Aschi stuck in his pocket a big bottle that looked as if it contained water, then dived again into the back of his tiny car, and started stuffing rags into his shirt until he bulged like Santa Claus.

"What are those for?" I asked.

"Bees, doctor. The tree has a nest of stingless bees. I brought the rags and chloroform from the laboratory." He tapped his hip pocket.

"Humph," I muttered. "Why the fuss about stingless bees?" I had heard of them and wondered what kind of freak insect they were.

We picked up our stuff and started for the tree. It was not more than two hundred yards away and the walking was made easy by threading our course among bushes and some little trees that spread out like beach umbrellas.

As we approached the ceiba it made an impressive picture. It was on a hillside and behind it loomed a tropical background of dense rainforest. The trunk of the tree was about eight feet in diameter, and facing us was a triangular opening, the apex directed upward. Heavy cumulus clouds were obscuring the sun, but I figured that even with the dark forest background I could get a fine picture by mounting the camera on the tripod and giving the film a few seconds' exposure.

What surprised me was my guide's caution in approaching the tree. He cut a sapling and fastened on the end one of his rags, saturated with chloroform. Making a rush for the tree he elevated the rag and left it resting against the tubular protuberance that had been the base of a hollow limb which had broken off. Around this I could see circling forms of insects. With the rag in place Aschi came darting back.

"Run," he gasped.

"Why——?"

I received my answer in a split second when something hit my neck like a pebble from a bean shooter, then another hit my cheek and several my forearms. Each impact was followed by a sensation as if a glowing cigarette had been pressed against the spot. I ran, slapping at the insects frantically all the way, to the point where Aschi and the native boy had made a stand.

"Stingless bees?" I asked.

"They bite! The bites hurt worse than stings."

The boys sat down and waited for the chloroform to take effect. After five minutes we returned to the tree. There was no fooling the returning bees with the chloroform wad. Those in the nest might have been subdued, but the legions in the air, coming from outside, were piling up in an insect traffic jam and swinging around the tree like débris at the base of a whirlwind. From this swirl they shot out radially, and came at us with that same bean-shooter effect. We retreated again.

"The chloroform is no good," exclaimed Aschi, clawing a bee out of his hair.

"We'll try smoke," was my suggestion. "I know what it does to northern bees."

With a plan in mind for making a particularly efficient smudge, I took the boys back to the cars where we removed the plug from a differential casing and by running a branch into this, then wiping it off on some rags, we converted them into black and oozy layers. I figured that this mess, divided into two installments would last during the capture of the bats.

The evil smudge arising from the first firing of the

rags had a marked effect upon the bees. They rose to greater heights and we were only occasionally pelted and bitten. The boys advanced on the tree carrying the net over their heads and looking like ghosts. I took one look up the shaft. There was another pair of *Vampyrus* looking like inverted opossums.

My job was now on the outside keeping the smudge going. I had set up the tripod for a time exposure, but it suddenly rained in torrents. Fortunately the smudge stayed lit under the protecting foliage of the tree.

The jointed sticks reached the bats. I heard Aschi's voice: "There's one in the cage." Then there was a curious muttering and shuffling. "Quick, quick," came Aschi's cry. "Get him in."

While I was wondering why the calm and efficient collector was so excited, the net was hurled aside and there boiled from the tree first the bat cage, then the boys. The cage contained two big bats which were rolling over and over in mad antics. The boys behaved in the same strange manner.

"Run! run!" gasped Aschi, scratching and digging at his head, arms and breast. Grabbing the cage, I nearly dropped it. A swarm of bees poured from the tree. There was an inner, backdoor entrance to their colony and the shaft of the ceiba had filled with them. As we dashed down the embankment I slipped on the clayey soil, now slimy with rain, and tobogganed a good ten feet with the bat cage. We stopped to rest under one of the umbrella-like trees.

I had spruced up a bit for this party, and I wished I hadn't. Trinidad clay is like red paint. I was plastered with it and with the black grease from the differential. But we had another pair of *Vampyrus spectrum* and some far-shot photographs.

Back at the professor's we built a travelling case and tried the experiment of putting both pairs of bats in it, and keeping an eye on them. There were several "perches" for them to hang from. Instead of the pairs suspending themselves separately, they always assembled in a cluster, their wings overlapping and forming a big, pear-shaped mass. Savage as they were in biting and snarling and gnashing out with their teeth at capture, there was no cage fighting. This was a bit surprising as we were now convinced that in a wild state they usually lived in single pairs. Nor were they nervous. If they were disturbed the four heads would protrude from the bottom of the mass, long ears would wriggle and pinkish faces would leer and peer about. Their appetites were not disturbed. We set traps for rats, and the bats discarded the tails of these rats in true *Vampyrus* fashion. They appeared to "check" in this habit.

The manipulation of heavy prey, while the bat hung inverted, was dexterous and remarkable. The hooks on the thumb joints of the wings of *Vampyrus* are particularly strong and sharp. They are heavier than the claws of a big domestic cat. With them the bats turned the prey about, shifted it into various positions, or even held it securely with one claw, the claw being capable of movements at its joint like a finger.

We decided that I could take better care of the two pairs of bats than of any more, and the time came to start north with them. I had also a collection of reptiles, the star of which was a young bushmaster. Curiously enough, it was the first infant bushmaster ever to go to a zoo, there being some mystery as to where the young of this outstanding species hide away.

My menagerie was placed aboard the R.M.S. *Nerissa* —the reptiles destined for the hold. The bat cage, disguised with panels of wrapping paper, was carried to my bathroom, where it barely went through the door. I knew there would be a battle later with the captain over rulings about pets in the cabins, but these bats were not pets, and their arrival for the first time in a zoo would be a big event. I wanted them right near me.

I stripped off my coat, heavy with perspiration. The job of getting that cage off a tender and up the narrow gangway of the ship in tropical heat, an hour before sailing time, was strenuous. I had staggered up the steep gangway, battling against down-coming and vociferous black porters. I didn't trust them among the motley array of shoving helpers that had carried my snake boxes and satchels. As they had reached the deck the porters seemed to go in different directions while I bumped and writhed through a milling crowd of sweating passengers and visitors. It was embarrassing to think that the bushmaster might be placed in somebody's cabin. Setting the bat cage in an alcove, I managed to round up my porters, classify the baggage and start the reptiles toward the hold. With my satchels where they belonged and the bat cage resting across the bathtub, I thought of how fine it would be to go to the very top deck where things were calm, and heave a few sighs of relief.

But this was not to be. A chattering started in the bat cage and grew louder until it sounded like a fight. It was time for the evening meal. The bats had been disturbed in getting them aboard. Placing them together had been experimental, and with those teeth, what damage could be done! There was danger of losing my prize captives right at the beginning. The only thing to do was to mollify them with food at once.

The professor had promised to send aboard the latest results of Aschi's shooting and trapping, and to have the collection placed in the ship's freezer. Working my way to the butcher shop I found it open and lighted but nobody in sight. While I was doing a dance of impatience a heavy door swung open and, in a cloud of steamy condensation and gush of cold, the butcher appeared. Yes, he had my crate of food, and I returned with it on the run.

The chattering was still going on full tilt and I felt decidedly worried as I ripped the paper from the cage. But there had been no bloodshed. Each bat was suspended separately and was leering out at me. There was much stretching of wings and scratching. I figured that these bats were pretty intelligent; it was past the feeding time adopted at the Urich laboratory and they knew it and were objecting.

When I opened the box from the freezer and unrolled some of the paper cylinders containing the food, I found an entirely different collection from what I had expected, mostly young rats. The bats grasped them readily enough, but I was disturbed to see the first round quickly disappear and to hear the chattering start louder than ever.

A second round satisfied them, but on counting the balance, I found that there were barely enough at this rate for two days. This was serious. The stops at West Indian ports are short, and I was afraid to feed the bats coarse-grained meat like beef, plenty of which could have been obtained on the vessel.

I still thought longingly of a breath of cool air on the upper deck—but not yet. So I made another trip to the butcher.

"At what port up ahead can I buy some pigeons?" I asked him.

"You can get a crate at Barbados, day after tomorrow."

The pigeons solved the problem and the butcher and I plucked two every night, which made a satisfying meal for the bats and quieted their chattering. They ate ravenously, even during rough weather. One night when the ship was rolling through a heavy swell and the dining room was almost deserted I zigzagged up the passageway with the pigeons, taking it for granted that the bats would be too disturbed by the motion of the ship to do more than dabble at their food.

They were suspended in a mass instead of being separated as was their custom with the approach of feeding time. Their pear-shaped bundle of bodies swayed like a pendulum as the vessel went over to port or starboard. I reached in with a half of a pigeon and a wriggling snout popped from the mass to seize the morsel. Within a couple of minutes they had separated and each bat hung swaying and devouring its respective portion.

From the pier the reptiles went to the Park in a truck, with the exception of the precious young bushmaster. It and the bats were not to be trusted out of my sight, so I hunted for a taxi with a door wide enough to admit the bat cage. While the space left for me made it necessary to sit in an exceedingly uncomfortable position during the long ride, I was happy. The bats were in perfect condition.

A crowd of newspaper men with cameras waited for me, for the news had been flashed by cable from the Virgin Islands about the first giant bats ever to leave their tropic habitat for exhibition in a zoo. The news even went to London, since the specimens had been captured in a British possession. The bats stuck out their grotesque heads at the photographers and some good close-ups were taken.

It didn't take long to build a sort of flying cage for

the *Vampyrus* group, and in this we placed their travelling cage; the door was removed and they were allowed to come out as they pleased. But, curiously enough, they regarded the smaller cage as a proper day shelter and while they prowled all around the larger cage at night, we would find them each morning back on their old perch. This went on for weeks until one day when we ushered them out, they went to the top of their high quarters, prowled about and selected a spot from which to hang. The supposition might be that they just happened to stop there, but they continued to return to that precise spot month after month.

They have grown tame enough to take their food from the keeper's hand and to look interestedly down upon the daily cleaning of the enclosure, but they will brook no close familiarity, and they snap at one's empty fingers if a hand gets too close, or resort to their habit of grinding their teeth. However, they are not nearly so nervous as the series of vampire bats, and that blood-drinking crowd has now been on exhibition over two years.

In the summer of 1936—on the fourteenth of July, to be exact—there was a big event in the *Vampyrus* family. A baby was born, and its wingspread was about fourteen inches. It was quite devoid of hair, pinkish gray, with a network of bright blood vessels traced all over its wings. It clung to the mother in an inverted position, thus nursing from her single pair of nipples, for the members of the group to which *Vampyrus* is related have but a single pair of nipples and seldom give birth to more than one baby. This is in contrast to the smaller, insect-eating bats that have as many as five in a litter which are carried by the mother in her nocturnal flights until they are nearly full grown and are together a burden of far greater weight than the parent.

With my opportunity to watch the developing young of *Vampyrus*, it was possible to see clearly, with this big species, various manifestations that could not be observed with small and nervous bats. The baby continued to nurse until it was three months old, when it began to share food with the mother. By that time it was two-thirds grown and well clad in lustrous brown hair. A month later it was seen to be independently hooked to the perch the greater part of the time, parental care being limited to preening it as a cat does her kittens.

A surprising thing during the development of this youngster was the solicitude of the father, who, whenever the mother's wings were unfurled from their protective clasp, would lick the baby from head to stern. By the latter part of September we decided that the young bat was conducting itself on its own.

In summarizing my notes about *Vampyrus* the following points stand out: their ravenous habit of pouncing upon food and the strength of their jaws in crushing the skulls of small animals, which indicates that they are savage killers when they are hunting their food. Contrasted with this is their good nature among themselves; if they are plentifully fed there seem to be no peevish traits, no squabbling over food in spite of their carnivorous nature. Moreover, they are the cleanest bats I have ever seen, markedly differing from other members of their order in being free from visible parasites.

This rather exhaustive account of *Vampyrus* brings out a point which prompted me to write it at length. It relates to the fact that much can be learned to produce revision and correction among natural history books without the necessity of plunging into exhausting and costly trips through wilderness areas. In the tropics, the edge of the jungle in many areas shades peoples' backyards. In the case of *Vampyrus*, our specimens were caught literally in backyards. I am not afraid of wilderness trips and I have gone on them, but in each instance I felt that I lost time in making shelters at camps and in experiencing fatigue in lugging accessories. Short trips of a day or two from a fairly civilized base have with me produced far better results and given me opportunity to do some of the things my friends declared impractical because of the attending waste of time. I made just such a trip last summer and I will tell about it in a later chapter.

Chapter XIV

SNAKE NURSERY

As an important part of the Trinidad trip, the young bushmaster deserves the place of prominence in a separate chapter. At the time I am writing this, it has broken all records among the zoos of the world where the species has been exhibited.

I did not capture this bushmaster; it was presented to me. I have been uniformly unsuccessful in capturing a specimen of this largest and most spectacular of the viperine snakes. I trailed the bushmaster through the hot jungles of Panama, where United States engineers were building the Madden Dam up the Chagres River. These men advanced like skirmishers through the dense tangle, surveying, sounding and drilling. They had killed a dozen bushmasters, and after I got there they continued to encounter them, but always when I was not there, although we prowled into all sorts of likely-looking spots, day and night. The following year, while I was in Trinidad, a fair-sized bushmaster, about eight feet long, was snared as it entered an outpost engine room of an oil company. It was given to me and I brought it to New York. Like all bushmasters that had been taken to zoos, it refused to eat. I force-fed it by sliding skinned rats down its throat with a long pair of forceps. The procedure was not pleasant, particularly when my fingers came close to a pair of fangs an inch long. I was between the devil and the deep blue sea, however, for at last I had a bushmaster on exhibition, with people coming to see it, and I couldn't let it starve. It died from lingulid worms piercing its lungs, which probably would have been its fate had it been left in its native wilds, for in its home environment it had eaten some rodent infested with these parasites that do little harm to the mammal but are dangerous in the interiors of snakes.

I have long been convinced that the reason why captive bushmasters fail to eat or to take the slightest interest in food is the shock of capture. The bushmaster is a particularly temperamental snake. It will endeavor to drive a human intruder from its lair by advancing a slow series of loops, then making a mighty sweep of the head. If restrained, it fights desperately and once captured it will sulk in a corner of the cage for days, never moving from the spot, not even to approach a dish to drink. Disturbed in captive quarters, its smoldering anger flares up, with a repetition of the weaving coils and sweeping stroke. As it is the practice in the tropics in catching a bushmaster to use a snare on a long pole, it is safe to say that about every other bushmaster is choked to death, and that the survivors, since the tension of the noose is not released until they have been pushed into a deep bag, have had an experience which they never forget. Indeed they are often strained and permanently injured in capture, since their vertebral bones are more delicate than those of other snakes. That was why I wanted to tackle a wild bushmaster myself. I would have used no noose, but a blunt hook with which to guide the serpent to a bag held open by a ring. I figured that the reaction of my captive would be to sense interference but not to consider itself attacked, and that such a specimen, not shocked, would feed as a captive.

We discussed all this in Professor Urich's laboratory at Trinidad during the summer of 1934.

"If someone could catch a young one, it could be lifted on the end of a branch without any danger, and dropped into a bag," I suggested.

The professor said that this had been done by the late R. R. Mole, a naturalist on the island, but that the reptile appeared to have been injured before the capture. However, Mr. Mole, a careful and sympathetic man, eager to study the habits of the star snake of the island, coaxed it into a bag and put it in a glass-fronted cage. It voluntarily ate one mouse, but died a short time after. This was the only record of a captive bushmaster feeding voluntarily.

The conversation ended with the professor promising to offer a bounty for the "gentle" capture of a young bushmaster, but he was not confident that one would be found. A strange thing about the species is that the young are seldom seen; native workers report that while they have encountered an adult or two every season, years may go by without their seeing a young bushmaster. Unlike all other New World vipers, the bushmaster lays eggs, and the favorite spot in which to hide them seems to be an abandoned armadillo burrow. The freshly hatched young are about sixteen inches long and as thick as a man's little finger. That fact has been established by examining eggs which were nearly ready to hatch. The eggs were opened and the young snakes measured. Where the young snakes go after hatching is a mystery. They may lurk in the armadillo burrows and come out only at night; and there is little human prowling after dark in areas inhabited by bushmasters.

When I returned to Trinidad in 1935 on the giant bat reconnoiter, the professor came aboard the steamer immediately after we anchored, and told me at once that he had a young bushmaster for me, and that it had already eaten *twenty-five* mice. His story of its capture showed how important specimens may be found in the tropics far from a lurid background. The giant bats had been discovered in backyards. The young bushmaster was discovered in a frontyard.

Not far behind the plantation area of Trinidad is a district known as Arima. Behind it are luxuriantly wooded hills. At the base of the slope is the pretty estate of Mr. and Mrs. Paul Urich. Mr. Urich is the German Consul. His wife is sympathetically interested in the wild life of the island, including everything from four-legged animals to snakes and orchids. An occasional bushmaster had been seen on this estate and the Urichs had discussed my wish to obtain a juvenile bushmaster. Word had gone around at Arima to watch for the desired specimen, and to capture it in a way that would not ruffle its feelings.

On the 2nd of February, 1935, one of the plantation hands notified Mrs. Urich that the long sought prize had been found, and led her to the spot. On the ground was a big leaf that had fallen from a palm. It was concave and attached to it was a stiff dry stem two feet long. In the center of the palm leaf was coiled a young mapepire, or bushmaster. Its coil was round and symmetrical and might easily have fitted within the inside ring of a saucer.

The transportation of this infant to the house, if it didn't get temperamental, would be a simple matter. Moving the leaf was like carrying a long-handled frying pan. The youngster did nothing more than rear its head and look interested. It was slid into a hat box and word of what had happened was carried to the professor. By the time the reptile arrived at his laboratory, he had constructed a glass-fronted case. The snake glided from the hat box to the case, and the professor issued stern warnings to his assistant that there was to be no tapping on the glass or disturbing the captive in any way. A drinking pan was placed inside. Because of the peculiar weaving motions of this serpent's head—

the neck rising obliquely and the head pointing almost at a right angle—the professor was reminded of the hand motions of an Egyptian dancer and, deciding that such a notable specimen should have a name, he christened it "Cleo," inspired by the thought of the famous Egyptian queen.

The professor thought that since Mole's young bushmaster had eaten a mouse that type of diet would be what was necessary, so he sent Aschi to get mice. That ingenious young man constructed a trap to catch mice alive, since no manufactured mouse trap could be found on the island. But in spite of the introduction of fresh mice, Cleo refused to eat. It looked as if the young bushmaster under the observation of Mole would hold the world's record by having voluntarily eaten a single mouse.

However, exactly two months after her capture Cleo ate a mouse.

To show me just what had happened up to the time of my arrival in Trinidad, the professor made a note of this important event. One more mouse and Cleo would break the world's record for captive bushmasters.

Trinidad mice are lean, since the tropic heat stunts the race. Next day another mouse was offered. To the professor's gratification, it was consumed and Cleo became the world's record bushmaster, but when she took a third mouse the following day and a fourth the next, her able chaperon and nurse could not restrain himself from mentioning the fact, and the achievement got into the Trinidad papers with the joshing question as to whether it was proper to call a female serpent a bushmaster or even a bushmistress when she was less than two feet long.

To indicate how the professor fed the baby on the mice that Aschi caught, I append the following from his notes, which he gave me before I left Trinidad; several of the later feedings occurred while I was there:

	Mice Eaten		*Mice Eaten*
April 2	1	July 24	1
April 3	1	August 1	1
April 4	1	August 2	1
April 5	1	August 10	1
April 11	2	August 14	1
May 3	1	August 15	1
May 6	1	August 25	shed skin
May 14	1	August 26	1
May 20	shed skin	August 28	1
June 1	1	August 29	1
June 2	1	September 9	1
June 11	1	September 28	1
June 19	1	September 29	1
June 26	1	October 1	1
July 14	1	October 3	1

On October 6th the bushmaster was locked in a travelling bag and we started for New York, arriving at the Park on October 14th. She took her first mouse on October 25th, about three weeks after the last feeding in Trinidad. The schedule of feeding and shedding the skin during the exhibition in New York and up to this time continues in line with the notes made in Trinidad:

Date	Mice Eaten	Date	Mice Eaten
October 25	1	May 9	1
October 31	1	May 22	1
November 5	1	May 27	1
November 10	1	June 6	1
November 15	shed skin	June 16	shed skin
November 15	1	June 17	1
December 16	1	June 24	1
December 23	1	June 30	1
January 3	1	July 13	shed skin
January 23	shed skin	July 14	1
January 25	1	July 22	1
February 7	1	July 27	1
February 15	1	August 1	shed skin
February 21	1	August 11	1
February 27	1	August 17	1
March 7	shed skin	August 24	1
March 9	1	September 7	shed skin
March 18	1	September 8	1
March 25	1	September 12	2
March 31	1	September 22	1
April 17	1	October 1	shed skin
April 30	1		

Note: Total feedings to time of writing: 65 times, with ten sheddings of skin from time of capture. Length at time of writing: approximately four feet.

In a summary of these observations the following points may be checked. The bushmaster seemed to sense a change in the development of winter and the artificial heating of a building, as she refused to eat between November 15th and December 16th. Again there was no inclination to eat from January 3rd to 23rd, and again from January 25th to February 7th. In all instances, it will be seen that casting the skin stimulated appetite, since the taking of food followed immediately or soon after.

In a European publication there has appeared a paragraph which contains the sentence: "Captive bushmasters soon die from casting trouble." There was no such trouble with the specimen under observation, since we concluded that dampness was necessary and placed a wet burlap bag in the cage whenever the reptile's eyes became clouded. This conversion of the cage into a humidor produced a perfect casting of the skin.

As has been seen, the snake averaged about one mouse a week. At the time of closing the record, a year and eight months after capture, Cleo is about four feet long, estimating her length by measuring the cast skin. This indicates that a period of about three years is necessary for a bushmaster to attain its "young adult" size. She was about sixteen inches long and half an inch in diameter at the time of her capture. Now she is two inches in diameter, a pale reddish brown, crossed by rhomboid bands of sooty black. During the spring and summer of 1936 she was provided with a sun-bathing cage of mesh, and was guided into this almost every day for sun and air on a broad window-sill of my office, for it is my contention that sunshine is the panacea for many captive animal ills and should be made available to all such creatures. As Head-Keeper Toomey says, "She is as fresh as they make them"—unafraid and inclined to weave into loops•if a stranger is present when she is being ushered into her sun-bathing enclosure. Readers may wonder why a scientist goes into all these details about an individual reptile. The explanation is that natural history is founded upon such detailed observation, and that authentic observation is constantly revising and eliminating theory.

Since the bushmaster was too small to occupy one of the large glass-fronted cages in the Reptile House by herself, and was too rare to be put into a "colony" cage, she was exhibited under unusual conditions. It has long been my rule to place no poisonous snake in any of the smaller cages which have only medium-thick glass fronts. All poisonous reptiles are behind heavy glass. There is always a feeling of great responsibility in exhibiting dangerous reptiles. The public is fascinated in looking at them and reading the descriptive labels, but the thought of the caretaker prevents the possibility of interested thrusts of canes or umbrellas.

Cleo went into one of the smaller cases for harmless serpents, but her case was placed inside one of the larger cases. In this way she appeared on a sort of pedestal, with a large label making clear her importance. The big case, however, was soon to be transformed into a snake nursery.

On the 15th day of January, 1936, Albert Vida, chief radio operator of the Motorship *City of New York*, plying between New York and South African ports, arrived with a shipment of snakes. Vida follows his interest in natural history as a diversion and is well known for his sympathetic treatment and careful packing of specimens for the long voyage of the fine vessel on which he travels. Also, on account of his genial good nature, the tropical fish fans have delegated him as a chaperon for their delicate pets. On every voyage coming west his radio room looks like a research laboratory, stocked with tanks and aerating apparatus. As usual, on this January trip he arrived with all his specimens alive, and we opened the snake cases with interest. The high spots in the shipment were a big Gaboon viper and three puff adders.

The Gaboon viper is one of the most sinister members of Africa's reptilian devilry. It does not grow longer than four feet, but a specimen of this size is as thick as a fire hose and has a head as broad as a man's hand. The pattern is reddish with a series of chocolate hour-glass markings down the back. On open ground one of these creatures looks like a strip of loud carpet, but among the fallen leaves of a woodland floor the Gaboon viper is difficult to see—and it is a forest reptile. Its ominous looks are in keeping with its heavy fang mechanism. The puff adder, belonging to the same scientific genus, is almost as bad in looks, but not quite. Because of the showy nature of these eccentric creatures the zoölogical gardens always seek to have them in their collections of exotics, but they seldom arrive in America. In consequence, the price of a Gaboon viper, when purchased from an animal dealer, is in the neighborhood of fifty dollars, with the less decorative puff adder fetching from twenty-five to thirty-five dollars, according to its size.

On January 28th, less than two weeks after the arrival of Vida's specimens, the Gaboon viper gave birth to twenty-seven young. The ugly babies were twelve inches long and an inch thick. They hissed and blew like all of the members of their thick-bodied genus, and when they were but a few hours old they sounded like hot coals being spilled into water, when we inspected the cage.

While we were figuring out the increase in value in the Gaboon viper quarters, two of the puff adders produced a total of forty-one hissing babies. We now started figuring all over again, basing our new set of figures, of course, upon the rearing of sixty-eight valuable snakes. It was clearly necessary to establish a snake nursery at once. This meant similar conditions for exhibiting these poisonous broods as for the exhibition of the bushmaster—small cages, safely enclosed within a large one with heavy glass.

Four cages were made, each thirty-six inches long and a foot wide, and divided into three compartments, making twelve sections in all. Two cages were allotted to Gaboon vipers and two to puff adders. In each section of one cage we placed a single Gaboon viper, and in another two babies in each compartment. The puff adders were similarly divided. The idea of the singles and doubles was to discover whether solitary or companionable quarters would work better. This arrangement provided for nine specimens of each species. The cases were stacked in a column alongside the cage of the young bushmaster. The effect was of a four-story tenement house with occupants at all the windows. Large descriptive labels were put up and our visitors were much interested.

The balance of the three litters was sent to the reptile curators of several of the large zoos, for I knew we would have enough trouble in obtaining eighteen half-grown mice each week for the nursery, without attempting to feed any more of the babies. Each compartment had a tag at the back on which to note the food that was accepted. All the young snakes shed their skins and started to eat. Their schedules turned out to be similar to that of Cleo. From the way they had developed it appears that we will have Gaboon vipers and puff adders for a long time to come.

The young of snakes are born or hatched at a specific time of the year—the late summer in temperate zones which give them time to become strong and attain some growth before they hibernate. The breeding period is in the early spring. The numbers of viviparous and egg-laying snakes are about fifty-fifty. Both poisonous and non-poisonous snakes are viviparous or oviparous. The pythons, cobras, rat snakes and local species, such as our common blacksnake, milk snake and green snake, lay eggs anywhere in number from one to several dozen, which hatch in from six to eight weeks' time. The eggs have a soft, leathery shell, creamy white in color. As the young snake develops within the egg, it grows a sharp little spike on its nose, the "egg tooth." This is used in slashing an opening in the tough shell and is shed off with the first skin. The infant glides off fully able to take care of itself. The only care it may receive from the parent is her coiling about the developing eggs to keep them moist, but even this is not invariable.

The viviparous snakes give birth to their young in much the same way as warm-blooded animals. Such litters stroll off in the same bold fashion as the egg-laying species, the mother paying no attention to them. If they are found near the mother it is incidental—the spot is to their liking and there is an abundance of food. The killing of a snake about to give birth to living young has been largely responsible for the story that snakes swallow their young to protect them. I have never seen any indication of such a trait.

Viviparous snakes may have astonishing numbers of young. Large litters indicate Nature's provision to perpetuate a species where the young undergo various hazards as they grow. The common water snake may have a litter of as many as fifty, and I counted seventy-two young in a litter of fer-de-lance in Honduras. Among the viviparous snakes there are both poisonous and harmless kinds. The rattlesnake, copperhead, and water moccasin give birth to young in the same way as do the common and harmless water snake, the garter snake, and diminutive brown snake.

The infant poisonous snakes go out into the world with perfect fang and venom gland equipment. Though the baby snake is only a miniature of the parent, yet the high toxicity of the lethal fluid they store, though it is only a few drops, was proved by an experience of the former head-keeper of the Zoölogical Park, Charles Snyder. He was removing a litter of fer-de-lance babies from the large cage occupied by the parent. The day was warm and Snyder was perspiring. One of the little snakes struck at him and a droplet of poison flew upon his forearm. At the moment he thought little of it and continued the job. The incident was recalled to him by a stinging pain. Examining his arm he noticed an abrasion, toward which the perspiring surface had carried a minute quantity of the poison. The bruise was washed with permanganate of potassium, but Snyder had a bad arm for several days.

Very young snakes naturally select quite different food from their parents. The young of species that in adult stage feed upon the larger rodents and birds, seek immature rodents of the smallest kinds. The young of some of the smaller species feed upon the soft-bodied larvae of insects, and quite a few that in later life may eat frogs and mice, live upon earthworms, crickets and grasshoppers. There are kinds that cannot be reared in captivity, since the food of the young snakes has not been discovered, in spite of every imaginable type of diet being offered to them.

Some of the smaller kinds of snakes attain maturity when they are about two years old. The medium sized species require about three years. Pythons and boas grow more slowly and are usually of breeding age when they are about five years old. Such young adults lay small numbers of eggs. From this stage they continue to grow slowly and only with ripening maturity produce larger litters. Rattlesnakes add about three rings to the rattle each year, acquiring, or uncovering a segment with each casting of the skin. My record observation of a rattler was made on a Florida diamondback, born in captivity, which acquired eleven segments in two years.

Most snakes breed infrequently in captivity, yet, curiously enough, of all species the most inclined to breed and produce litters of healthy babies are the rattlesnakes and American water moccasin. The lives of these reptiles are fairly long, some specimens living more than thirty years.

The world is a big place with many interests, but gossip in similar institutions runs the rounds, flashing across the Atlantic between American and European zoos. The fact that Cleo, the successfully nursed bushmaster, is establishing a record is pretty widely known among the reptile houses. At the rate she is growing, she may soon graduate from the nursery.

Chapter XV

THE PARADOX FROG

Many experiences have come my way since the episode of the thousand flies, but a seed of interest was sown back in those days, and my notes on frogs have grown.

Biologically speaking, frogs, toads, and their relatives in eccentric development are hangovers from a period of the *excessively* dim past. Countless millions of years ago, life emerged from the waters to pioneer upon terrain that had been untenable because of volcanic heat. The transition from deep-water forms to creatures of the shallows was slow; then came writhing through mud and the experiment of gulping air. Fishes to amphibians, amphibians to reptiles—that was the change through aeons of time. As if to make clear to moderns what was stretched out over a long period, Nature has handed down the transition from aquatic tadpole to air-breathing frog and toad—a story from the ages presented like a play, within a period of months. But some of her subjects have become restless as demonstrators. The tale of what has happened is a strange one.

It was interest in the life history of a frog which has long puzzled scientists that brought about my trip to Trinidad during the summer of 1936. The scientific name of that frog is *Pseudis paradoxis*. Translating the Latin freely this means the paradoxical frog, creature of extreme eccentricity. It begins as a giant and changes into a dwarf.

Not many years ago, relatively speaking, scientists discovered enormous tadpoles in certain lakes of Venezuela and in a single lake, really a pond, on the near-by Island of Trinidad. These tadpoles grew to a length of fourteen inches. As a basis for comparison, it is worthy of note that the tadpoles of the huge bullfrogs of the lower Mississippi Valley attain a length of only six to eight inches. When this giant larval form of a tropical frog was discovered, it was thought permissible to give a scientific name to this extraordinary species, even though the adult, or frog form had not been found. There were theories as to where it had its lair—that it retreated into inaccessible swamps or that it burrowed into the débris of the jungle floor and came forth at night, a trait not uncommon among tropical frogs. Little did those early scientists dream that a small, iridescent green frog which hopped in and out of the very ponds so intensively ransacked for the giant tadpoles, was what they sought.

That discovery was made in recent years. It is now established that the tadpole of *Pseudis paradoxis* grows to gigantic size, but when it starts to sprout hind and forward limbs and stick its snout out of the water to speed the transition from aquatic creature to air-breathing frog, it shrinks amazingly. All that remains from a fourteen-inch tadpole is a two-inch frog. Along came theories about the collapse of glands or change in coördination of glands—and the gland theory, relating to growth, now seems to be pretty well established, even explaining humans, fat or thin, tall or short.

Strangely enough, the established life history of *Pseudis* seems to be based largely on collections of specimens which immediately found their way into cans of preserving solution carried afield by investigators. So far as I know, the only tadpoles collected and kept alive were in the hands of my good friend, Professor F. W. Urich, who has done so much to help me during my collecting in Trinidad.

He told me that he had kept the tadpoles under observation in the shrinking stage, but had found them extremely delicate. From his curtailed observations, he estimated that shrinkage in length was as much as an inch a day. His specimens would eat nothing but rotted lettuce. So far as I could ascertain no living tadpoles of *Pseudis* had ever been collected to be taken from the country of their natural habitat.

The conference with the professor took place when I was about to leave Trinidad with the giant bats. The objective of bringing out another rare type and landing it in a zoo alive meant going to Trinidad the next year, so I told my friend he would see me back again.

Life history of the common frog and the toad. The tail is not dropped off but absorbed while the mouth parts are changing. The cycle is prolonged with the frog, which develops in deep water. That of the toad is rushed as the eggs are laid in rain pools.

A developing albino frog. Such freaks have a poor chance to attain maturity as they are conspicuous objects for attack.

The common toad. It carelessly lays its eggs in shallow, evaporating rain pools, leaving the young to face many hazards. The solution to its preservation is the number of eggs, 5,000 or more. Not one in a hundred produces an adult.

Australian tree toad. Among such highly specialized kinds there have developed keen methods of protecting the young; hence small numbers of eggs are laid. Some species deposit their eggs high in the trees, in hollows of leaves, the eggs imbedded in aqueous froth.

When the time came to return in September of 1936, some newspaper friends wanted to know what I was after. I outlined the history of the paradox frog. What I didn't tell them was that the only pond on the island where the creatures were to be found was within view of a plantation house; that all the help I needed was to be had for the asking. True enough, I might have painted a picture of the great Nariva mangrove swamp, the edge of which was not many minutes' hike from the pond, where huge anacondas and crocodilians were common enough, but that would have been laying it on in a way that is reprehensibly used by amateur explorers. It was enough to say that Mayaro and the pond could be reached by motor car. The only "hazards" I could think of, but didn't mention, were breakdown of the car in traversing the trail along the Nariva swamp and a bad session with mosquitoes, or being caught by the tide in running a long stretch of beach, and having the automobile imbedded over the wheels in sand.

Again on the *Nerissa,* with thoughts of New York fading, and a chance to consider calmly the quest ahead, there was an afternoon in the smoking room when I reviewed what I had learned about frogs since the episode of the flies. My only companion was a tall glass of liquid, which appeared to stimulate a goodly train of thoughts.

What were the high points of interest about frogs and toads, of which there are over one thousand and five hundred kinds? These were evidenced in their breeding habits. All started life as tadpoles, but what variety there was in the speed of growth, in the conditions of their watery cradle, the solicitude or utter indifference of the parent; the provisions laid down by Nature to counterbalance this indifference, so that many species might not be rapidly wiped out! There isn't much physical difference between frogs and toads, but it is among the latter that the points I had in mind are particularly evident. The common toad, for instance, lays as many as five thousand eggs. Yet there are tropical species that lay less than a dozen eggs. Why this great discrepancy? In spite of it the tropical species seem to be as numerous as the northern one.

That was because of all sorts of dangers surrounding the eggs, then the minute tadpoles, and threatening the transformed young of the care-free toad of temperate climes. Here were instances of evolutionary processes in the perpetuation of species. With some frogs and toads the instinct to protect the young in some way has become highly developed. With others, as time has gone on, a laxity of care has become evident. The common toad lays its several thousand eggs in spring rain pools, in open places. There is danger of evaporation, nothing but a puddle to be left where a huddle of surviving tadpoles could transform into air-breathing toadlets. Such open pools are magnets for the types of insects that are partially aquatic and seek such delectable morsels.

Transformation of the common toad, however, is

very rapid, a matter of a few weeks against many months or several years for frogs, the tadpoles of which grow rapidly as swift swimmers and as a rule begin life in permanent bodies of water. The toad tadpoles begin to grow legs when barely half an inch long. When they have absorbed the tail, they are mere miniature toads. A half dozen could crowd on the top of a dime. Those lucky enough to develop and leave the rainpool go hopping through the open and into all sorts of dangers. It has been estimated that far less than one per cent of the eggs of the toad produce an adult.

But what a difference among kinds which by some mysterious influence have developed opposite habits from their relatives in perpetuating the species!

A few frogs and toads are strictly aquatic; they never leave the water and have enormously developed hind feet for fast swimming. With one of these native to northern South America, the Surinam toad, the protection of the young is provided for in a fantastic manner. When the eggs are laid the male presses them into cavities on his mate's back. With honeycombed dorsal surfaces, the female goes about while miniature tadpoles transform within the craters which eventually release the fully-formed but tiny toads, which, with their excessively developed rear-foot webbing can dart through the water and evade enemies.

Most of the tropical frogs and toads have acquired habits of caring for the young in some way and have cut down on the number of eggs deposited. The tadpoles of *Dendrobates*, a small but decorative frog, hatch in rainpools but the father stands by watching for the possible evaporation of the pool or its invasion by enemies. If anything happens he enters the water and his progeny quickly gather. By means of suckers beneath the head, they attach themselves to his back. With the family aboard he is off to another and better pool where his vigil continues until there is a transformation of froglets which burrow into the jungle mould and so hide from enemies as they grow.

Leptodactylus, a genus of large tropical frogs represented by my "mountain chickens" of an earlier chapter, keep their tadpoles in shallow water until the young are ready to take on rapid growth. The mother builds a circular dam of mud and within this lays her eggs. The provision is made before the seasonal rains set in. When the rains come on the progeny in the nursery are strong and ready to go. The torrential daily showers disintegrate the dam, but release tadpoles which can speed safely through deeper waters.

Even more cautious are species which carry the eggs in a throat pouch until they hatch and the tadpoles acquire strength and speed, when they are released in waters woven with protective weeds and algae. As examples of the most modern frogs, from the evolutionary point of view, are species with expanded digits or "suckers" for climbing, which lay their eggs high in the trees in hollows of leaves, the parent producing an aqueous froth which absorbs tropic moisture and thus provides a medium for tadpole development.

These are some of the strange breeding habits, between which are many modifications. But there are other points in this grouping of fifteen hundred members. Some of the frogs are minute, a half an inch long when fully grown, while there is one in Africa of such size that it can swallow a big rat. Another African member, called the dagger frog, has the bone of the thumb protruding in the form of a powerful claw which is thought to be used in cracking open the shells of crabs which form a large part of its food. There is mimicry among the tree-climbing species which causes them to look like patches of lichen. Some have poisonous skin secretions. *Hyla vasta* of Haiti, a tree toad, has burned collectors' hands like battery acid when it was handled. The tiny *Dendrobates* of South America have a skin secretion so deadly that the Indians use it in poisoning the darts for their blow guns. Colors run riot among these creatures. No more vivid tints of red, blue, or green could be imagined. Metallic sheens of gold, bronze and silver are also found. And with all of this are voices, roarings, bawlings, chatters, whistles so strident that miniatures of the clan can hurtle sounds more carrying and penetrating than members of the mammal clan a thousand times their bulk.

There was that interesting résumé from my friend Major Stanley Flower, of the Zoölogical Society of

London, who had painstakingly checked the duration of life of frogs and toads. The listing of his records in comparing the notes of widely separated institutions with the best facilities for maintaining amphibians showed a remarkable similarity.

The records of even the smallest frogs and toads were surprisingly long. Specimens of the miniature European fire-bellied toad lived as long as thirteen years and a European natterjack toad, fifteen years. The tree frogs also carried records up to sixteen years, being rivalled among the tailless amphibians by similar records of the American bullfrog. Among other frogs with long records were the species of *Leptodactylus* of the American tropics. The longest records among these were held by specimens from Panama in the New York Zoölogical Park, now on exhibition for more than twelve years. That these periods do not represent the ultimate length of life of amphibians was indicated by a note about the common European toad, which read:

> Having re-examined the question of the toad mentioned by Pennant in his "British Zoology" . . . I consider that the statement that this animal lived for at least thirty-six years can be accepted as true and also that it was becoming feeble from old age, although the immediate cause of his death was the injuries that it received from a tame raven.

But how about my prospective prize? A green island was floating by. I was nearing Trinidad.

Aside from the mammoth tadpoles, what was there

of interest about *Pseudis paradoxis?* Was there anything remarkable about the frog itself?

Yes. It had a grasping thumb—of all things for a frog! Some scientists have asserted that the development of such a thumb among the apes had given rise to the human race. At any rate it hadn't helped *Pseudis* very much in its mixed-up development in growing down instead of up, although it was alleged that it maintained comfortable positions in the water by grasping aquatic plants.

Arriving at Trinidad I was distressed to learn that the friend of so many scientists, Professor Urich, had suffered a paralytic stroke. I hastened to see him and learned that it was expected that he would be up and around again in a few months. I had expected to visit parts of the island with which he was especially familiar, but I was now determined to spend as much time with him as was possible, and so I confined all thoughts of collecting to the trip to Mayaro and seining for the tadpoles of *Pseudis*.

Mr. and Mrs. Paul Urich went ahead to Mayaro to collect some of the workers at their coconut plantation to give me a hand. J. P. L. Wehekind, keen naturalist and collector, went in my car taking various utensils that might be of use.

The Urich plantation house is in a perfect tropical setting. It looks out on a palm-fringed beach that stretches for miles, where a human, except perhaps a native fisherman, is seldom to be seen. Behind it, and also stretching for miles, is a broad band of coconut palms and behind these looms the great Nariva mangrove swamp. In front of the house, close to the beach —in fact, so close as to be salinated by ocean spray, is a pond which appears to be there for no earthly reason. It has no more area than the type of backyard seen behind congested houses, but it is permanent water. Immediately behind the house is a slightly larger pond, but still small enough so that a hat could easily be tossed across it. These two miniature water pockets are the only ponds for miles and they are the sole spots in Trinidad where *Pseudis* is to be found. No tadpoles of the species have as yet been seen in the little pond near the beach, although the frogs occur in it. Both tadpoles and frogs live in the pond behind the house. It is supposed that this strange species arrived in Trinidad on driftwood from Venezuela, which seems plausible when one looks out on an ocean stained to golden-green by the not distant outpouring of the Orinoco.

We checked the little pond by the ocean to see if it contained the tadpoles. The frogs were there, but no *Pseudis* tadpoles, although there were numerous tadpoles of a tree frog which lives among the palms. The larger pond contained the tadpoles I was after, but all we brought up in a number of seinings were very small, barely three inches long, and these immature members were extremely gelatinous and delicate. It was difficult to remove them from the net and transfer them to the

Dendrobates, a full-grown frog of South America, with highly toxic skin secretion used by the Indians in poisoning the darts for their blowguns.

A bullfrog from the Louisiana low grounds, with body eight inches long, engulfing a young chicken.

Why an isolated and miniature fresh-water pond should exist at the edge of a tropic beach is a mystery—but so is the species of frog living in this water pocket.

The outlines of this *Pseudis* tadpole coming up for air are commonplace enough, but the specimen was of great interest and drew more attention on arriving in New York than a jungle beast in barred quarters.

collecting pail without injury. Several were soon floating stomach up, dead. There was no mistaking this species of tadpole. The tail has a particularly wide swimming flange, top and bottom,, and is strongly marked with black spots. Also, the mouth projects forward instead of downward as is usual with tadpoles. By the time the day was coming to a close I had a fair series of uninjured specimens, the largest of which was five inches long. Our efforts convinced us that there were no big tadpoles in the pond, a situation which might point to *Pseudis* breeding only at scattered periods; possibly this had been a breeding year, and a considerable time was necessary before the progeny in the pond attained large size.

Several of the adult, iridescent frogs were seined, but I tossed them back to conserve them. There was plenty of evidence that this was necessary, as the pond was subject to invasion by young caymans from the Nariva swamp and the presence of carnivorous eels was well attested to by our net hauls. Definite protection of this interesting spot was discussed. We went into specifications about making eel traps and methods of catching the little caymans, which are midway in form between alligators and crocodiles.

The sixty-mile trip to Port-of-Spain was disastrous. The immature amphibians were unable to withstand the jolting of the car. Rushing into salvage work on arriving at my quarters, I found that all were dead with the exception of the five-inch specimen. The survivor was placed in a washbasin. This was a depressing conclusion for a collecting trip—one tadpole. The deceased examples were preserved in alcohol as museum specimens.

That single tadpole proved to be a star actor and gave me a leg to stand on when I returned to New York, although it threw antics which pointed to *Pseudis* being even more eccentric than I had thought.

Going to inspect it the morning after the trip, I was shocked, interested and dubious about what kind of tadpole I had. It had been five inches long the night before. Now it was three inches long. Floating in the basin was a speckled cornucopia. Trailing this around with a broomstraw I discovered that the cornucopia was without the remotest doubt a casting of the tail covering. What did this indicate? Was it possible that *Pseudis* grew in leaps to shrink and grow again? There seemed to be little chance for careful scientific checking, with only one tadpole!

After several trials the lone specimen was induced to eat rotted lettuce and toward this it turned voraciously. On that diet it reached New York, meanwhile acquiring a rapid growth of tail to replace the shed portion.

As the *Nerissa* lay at quarantine my newspaper friends boarded the steamer and asked what I had brought back. There was a hearty laugh when it was discovered that my spoils consisted of a single tadpole, but the story of *Pseudis* was interesting and they wrote it up. At least I had made the try, and a representative of the species had been brought for the first time from the tropics.

The tadpole was photographed in a compressed, crystal tank. To my surprise—and apprehension—it shed off another cornucopia. It became shorter, though it retained its body bulk. It was again photographed and died, I think, of photography. At any rate I had some notes, though I am still in doubt as to what might have happened if the specimen had survived. It was immature, but why should it shrink at that stage? The answer lies in that pond at Trinidad.

Things had been swinging through a bit of a grind and I wanted some recreation around home. It was autumn and I couldn't get away again so soon. The very thing occurred to me—to take off the left bank of cylinders of my car. There had been a murmur and I'd traced it with an engine stethoscope; valves possibly. The investigation looked intriguing.

I spent an hour boring through a ceiling beam in the garage for an eye-bolt to swing block and tackle and hoist the heavy cylinder casting. The pulley was hooked into the eye, and the hood of the car was off when my wife appeared. She asked what I was doing, and I told her that I was looking for relaxation.

"It will take much longer than sending the car to the service station," she suggested.

"But I'm going to enjoy this."

"We'll have to cancel social engagements for a week."

"That's good, but why?"

"To get your hands in presentable shape."

The maid brought out sandwiches when I sent in word that hands and overalls would be in no condition to touch doorknobs or brush contact with dining room chairs. My meal tasted good though it was flavored with oil.

Curiously enough, at such moments one's memory is particularly active. With me my thoughts were probably started by a glance at the car's dash. Weather instruments had been installed. This car was powerful, fast and could go places, and get there in time. There was a commodious trunk for suit cases. With this car there would be no repetition of the Palm Beach hurricane fiasco. Missing that storm had left a rankling memory. What had been my greatest disappointments? There had been a number, but mitigating circumstances or later fulfillment of desires made many of them hazy in my memory.

Going back from recent years to boyhood, I recalled four major disappointments: The failure to catch a big bushmaster in Panama; missing the Palm Beach hurricane; missing an eruption of Mt. Lassen—and missing the engines pumping during the fire at Quinn's Livery Stable.